A Field Guide to Alaska Grasses

Quentin D. Skinner

Stoney J. Wright   Robert J. Henszey

Joann L. Henszey   Sandra K. Wyman

ISBN 978-0-615-64886-6

Front Cover
Calamagrostis canadensis
(Bluejoint reedgrass)

Distributed by

Alaska Department of Natural Resources
Division of Agriculture
Alaska Plant Materials Center
5310 S. Bodenburg Spur Rd.
Palmer, AK 99645

2013 second printing funded by the
United States Department of Agriculture
Natural Resources Conservation Service

Table of Contents

Foreword

Alaska's position, size, and complex biogeographic history has created a flora of vicariant taxa, intercontinental biogeographic disjunctions, and, for this latitude, a high level of endemism. More recently, the Alaska region has been the arena for large-scale human activities, from exploration of mineral and oil, which are resulting in exponential anthropogenic change of global concern, such as changes related to global warming. New evidence suggests that climate-driven extinctions and range retractions are already widespread, and we are at the forefront of studying these changes in Alaska. Grasses are predicted to increase in early successional post-fire stands that will become more common near the forest margins, and in relatively xeric sites, if these sites happen to become drier as a result of a changing climate (Chapin et al. 1996).

The great diversity of native grasses in Alaska was recognized by early explorers, botanists, agronomists and others, and has been used in conjunction with other "cultivated" forage grasses from lower latitudes in Eurasia that have been brought north into Alaska during recent decades. As with many worthwhile projects, the *A Field Guide to Alaska Grasses* was a long time in the making. The dual challenge to the field guide's authors was to be technically correct and user friendly. It is very appropriate that the lead author should be Professor Quentin Skinner, whose account is the culmination of at least 35 years of interest in and study of the Poaceae. This is a natural extension of his *A Field Guide to Nevada Grasses* (together with Barry Layne Perryman, 2007) and Skinner's *A Field Guide to Wyoming Grasses* (2010), which are both very well-documented field guides and have been welcomed by all those who require an easy guide to grass identification in those states. The current tome will surprise you with its exceptionally well-illustrated color plates of each of the 167 taxa covered, detailed descriptions of the distinguishing features, distribution maps based on herbarium records in Alaska, keys to the tribes and genera of Poaceae, as well as keys to the species of larger genera such as *Agrostis, Bromus, Calamagrostis, Elymus, Festuca, Poa, Puccinellia* and many smaller genera. Quentin has made the job for anyone wanting to identify grasses in Alaska easy by dissecting out the minute florets, associated bracts, and spikelets. His skillful photographs and well-composed comparative plates will give anyone the tools needed to tackle identification of the notoriously difficult grasses.

Steffi Ickert-Bond
Associate Professor of Botany and Curator
of the Herbarium (ALA),
Museum of the North,
University of Alaska Fairbanks.

Studying grasses in Alaska, 2009

Preface

1962

2012

Jim Harrower   Quentin Skinner   Tony Oney

My appreciation for magnificent Alaska began as I served in the Army and on the U.S.A. Olympic Biathlon Training Unit at Fort Richardson from 1962 to 1965. While serving, Jim Harrower and Tony Oney (Alaska dentists, pilots, conservationists, and arctic guides and outfitters) took this fledgling 2nd Lieutenant under their guidance to teach him Alaska attributes that meant so much to them. I am blessed and grateful that fifty years later, I now have the opportunity to add to our friendship and their Alaska heritage by being an author of the new *A Field Guide to Alaska Grasses*.

Sandy Wyman (National Riparian Service Team, U.S. Bureau of Land Management) and I visited Alaska in 2007 to photograph and collect riparian zone grasses for a new book, *Grasses of Riparian Zones*. We visited Stoney Wright (Manager Alaska Plant Materials Center) in Palmer and Robert and Joann Henszey (Biologist, U.S. Fish and Wildlife Service, and Technician, University of Alaska Fairbanks (UAF), Alaska and Polar Regions Collections respectively) in Fairbanks for their input to our research and writing efforts. This visit also brought together friends that were all associated with, trained by, or worked with the late Allen A. Beetle - renowned Grass Taxonomist at the University of Wyoming (UW), and who also collected plants in Alaska with W.J. Eyerdam in 1939 and again from 1946-1949. During this visit, Sandy and I were asked to consider writing a field guide to grasses for Alaska to complement the field guides to Nevada (Perryman and Skinner 2007) and Wyoming (Skinner 2010). Writing a field guide for Alaska seemed logical, as many riparian and Wyoming grasses are also Alaskan grasses.

Our 2009 answer was yes, if all would serve as authors and a steering committee be named to help guide this project. Across four field seasons and 5 years (2007-2011) most all Alaska grass species have been photographed, collected, and where needed, compared to specimens in the University of Alaska Museum Herbarium (ALA), and the Rocky Mountain (RMS) and A.A. Beetle (WYAC) Herbariums at the University of Wyoming (UW). Distribution maps were developed for each species and brief descriptions provided for the users of this field guide.

A Field Guide to Alaska Grasses includes 167 grass species and subspecies, and is written to supplement the excellent taxonomic treatments presented in the recent and impressive *Flora of North America, Volume 24 (FNA, Vol. 24)* by Barkworth et al. (2007), as well as the Alaskan standby, *Flora of Alaska and Neighboring Territories* by Hultén (1968). Nomenclature, classification, species synonyms, and descriptions for Alaska grasses generally follow those in the *FNA, Vol. 24*. Species recognized in Hultén (1968), but considered synonyms in *FNA, Vol. 24,* are included because of past and accepted use in Alaska. The dichotomous keys follow clear separations presented by Hultén (1968), Cody (2000), Skinner (2010), and as a final source, Barksworth et al. (2007). Morphological measurements used for separations were updated to those presented by Barksworth et al. (2007). Photographic plates for each species were prepared to include detail of illustrations, and where appropriate and possible, key vegetative/floral characteristics described in the *FNA, Vol. 24*.

Four paragraphs are presented opposite a photographic plate for each species. The first paragraph is a stand alone description from tribe to species and is a supplement to the dichotomous keys found on pages 3-20. The second and third paragraphs detail vegetative and floral characteristics, which may repeat some plant characteristics from paragraph one. The fourth paragraph provides a brief ecological and historical description, while the Alaska maps provide detailed species distribution. The field guide also includes colored plates showing the morphology of grasses, a glossary, and index to help identify grasses in the field.

Quentin Skinner, Professor Emeritus, UW
Cumming, Georgia, June, 2012

Acknowledgements

The authors wish to acknowledge our Steering Committee for encouraging us to prepare this field guide. We thank these academics and professionals for their continuing guidance while selecting species to include in the field guide and for offering advice during the field guide's preparation: Dr. Dave Murray (Professor of Botany and Curator Emeritus, Herbarium (ALA), University of Alaska Museum of the North), Dr. Steffi Ickert-Bond (Associate Professor of Botany and Curator of the Herbarium (ALA)), Carolyn Parker (Research Professional, Herbarium (ALA), Jeff Mason (formally Ecologist, Colorado State University, Fort Wainwright/Donnelly Training Area), Gino Graziano (formally, Invasive Weeds and Agricultural Pest Coordinator, Alaska Plant Materials Center), Dr. Roseann Densmore (Research Ecologist, U.S. Geological Survey Alaska Biological Science Center), and Paul Krabacher (formally, Vegetation Program Leader, U.S. Bureau of Land Management, Alaska State Office).

Lee Koss (formally, Soil, Water, and Air and Riparian Programs Lead, U.S. Bureau of Land Management, Alaska State Office) was instrumental in facilitating the lead author's excursion to collect and photograph Alaska's riparian grasses in 2007, which later led to this more comprehensive field guide to Alaska's grasses. We appreciate the initiative of Megan Boldenow and Jeff Schively from the Alaska Chapter of the Society of Wetland Scientists for organizing and sponsoring two workshops to help raise awareness of Poaceae in Alaska, and the hospitality of our hosts for these workshops: the Alaska Plant Materials Center in Palmer and the ALA Herbarium in Fairbanks. Professional support during these workshops and in the field was provided by the Alaska Plant Materials Center's Lyubomir Mahlev (Agronomist), Phil Czapla (Agronomist), and Kathi VanZant (Seed Analyst). Assistance from Jordan Metzgar (Collections Manager and Ph.D. candidate, Herbarium (ALA)) while examining grasses in the ALA Herbarium was greatly appreciated, and our special thanks to the numerous unsung collectors who took the time to collect these specimens and submit them to the institutions listed in the Grass Distribution Map References.

Our sincere thanks to Leroy Gunderson, Sr. who gave two strangers a ride to the Meade River after our plane left the remote North

Slope village of Atqasuk. We especially appreciate Stanley Segevan's willingness to drop his work at a moment's notice and become our impromptu guide during our unannounced excursion to Atqasuk. We appreciated the hospitality of our hosts Berni and Uta Hicker from Arctic Getaway Cabin B&B in Wiseman, and the staff from Deadhorse Camp after our long days of collecting grasses along the Dalton Highway and in the Prudhoe Bay oilfield. Dr. Bill Streever (Environmental Studies Leader, BP Alaska) kindly facilitated our access into the restricted Prudhoe Bay oilfield to collect grasses.

Robert J. Soreng (Research Associate, Botany (NHB), National Musuem of Natural History, Smithsonian Institute (US)) kindly provided field photos for *Poa abbreviata* subsp. *pattersonii, Poa hartzii* subsp. *alaskana, Poa laxiflora, Poa porsildii, Poa pseudoabbreviata, Poa paucispicula, and Puccinellia vahliana*. Sharing his world expertise of the genera *Poa* and *Puccinellia* is sincerely appreciated.

We are grateful to our family, friends, and colleagues for allowing us to pursue this project rather than spending time with them, and for tolerating our sometimes protracted efforts to get just the right field photograph of a grass. The coauthors join Quentin in extending a special heartfelt thanks to Quentin's wife, Arlene Skinner, for allowing us to once again take precious time from their family to benefit others as she has done so often for well over 35 years of Quentin's teachings and projects.

Finally, this field guide would not have been possible without the support of the Alaska Department of Natural Resources, Division of Agriculture, Alaska Plant Materials Center; U.S. Forest Service, Alaska Forest Health Protection Program; U.S. Bureau of Land Management, Alaska Division of Resources; U.S. Natural Resources Conservation Service; U.S. Fish and Wildlife Service, Conservation Planning Assistance, and Habitat Restoration and Coastal Program; and University of Wyoming, College of Agriculture and Natural Resources, Department of Ecosystem Science and Management.

Robert Henszey, June, 2012
Fairbanks, Alaska

Grass Distribution Maps

Distribution maps for the grasses of Alaska were based on the databases maintained by herbaria collections, a database of exotic weeds in Alaska, and a limited number of personal and institutional collections (including the lead author) and study sites (please see the Grass Distribution Map References (next) for a complete list). Over 41,000 geographic references are in our database, which complements the more extensive data used for the Flora of North America maps (Barkworth et al. 2007, *http://herbarium.usu.edu/webmanual/*). If the locations for our data were distributed evenly across the 1,481,347 km² of Alaska's landmass, the result would be one collection per 36 km². Much of Alaska, however, remains remote and difficult to reach, so grasses tend to be collected where access is more convenient such as along Alaska's limited road system and near villages. Thus the distribution maps show where the species have been found, but not necessarily the full extent of their distribution. Still, the maps for the more widely distributed species such as *Calamagrostis canadensis*, *Deschampsia cespitosa* and *Festuca rubra* suggest collectors have covered much of Alaska.

Nomenclature follows *Flora of North America, Vol. 24* (Barkworth et al. 2007), supplemented by the synonymy in the *Catalog of New Wrold Grasses* (Soreng et al. 2011) when synonyms were not listed in Barkworth et al. (2007). I relied upon the collector and institution to properly identify species and their locations; however, I checked and corrected any locations greater than 0.4 km outside Alaska or its coastline. I also assigned coordinates to collections without coordinates, but with descriptions sufficient to assign coordinates reasonably close to the collected location, with the aid of the Geographic Names Information Service for the United States (*http://geonames.usgs.gov/pls/gnispublic*) and Google Earth (*http://www.google.com/earth/index.html*). Many of these assigned coordinates were associated with the early Alaskan expeditions, including two dating as far back 1827 when Ludolf Karl Adalbert von Chamisso collected *Poa stenantha* on Unalaska Island (Tropicos 2010), and Kyher [sic Kyber] collected *Calamagrostis canadensis* var. *langsdorffii* near Sitka (Smithsonian Institution 2011). Chamisso's contribution to early Alaskan botany is fairly well recognized, however Kyber appears to be the doctor/naturalist (Dr. Kyber/Kiber) who traveled with

Ferdinand von Wrangell on his expeditions in eastern Siberia and an 1825-27 around the world voyage (*The Literary Gazettte* 1827, Wrangell 1840, Polansky and Stanton 1986).

Maps were generated with ESRI's ArcGIS and projected in Alaska Albers Equal Area Conic, with a North American datum of 1983. The base map included data from Alaska Hydrography (1998), Alaska Major Rivers (1998) and GTOPO30 (1996). At the full extent of the Alaska map, a species dot is about 36 km in diameter, while at the closest extent a species dot is about 10 km in diameter.

Grass Distribution Map References

AKEPIC. 2011. Alaska Exotic Plant Information Clearinghouse database. Alaska Natural Heritage Program, University of Alaska, Anchorage. *http://akweeds.uaa.alaska.edu/*, 2011-02-17.

Bruce Bennett Personal Collection. 2010. Private collection maintained at Whitehorse, Yukon, Canada. 2010-04-26.

British Petroleum North Slope Long-term Monitoring Site. 2009. Database maintained by ABR, Inc., Fairbanks, Alaska. *http://abrinc.com/*, 2009-09-03.

Canadian Museum of Nature (CAN). 2010. Herbarium specimen data provided by personal communication. *http://www.nature.ca*, 2010-11-19.

Global Biodiversity Information Facility (GBIF) Data Portal. 2010. Herbarium specimen data provided by: Utah State University (UTC). *http://data.gbif.org*, 2010-12-31.

Pacific Northwest Herbaria. 2011. Herbarium specimen data provided by: Personal Herbarium of Bruce Bennett, and The New York Botanical Garden Virtual Herbarium (NY). *http://www.pnwherbaria.org*, 2011-01-02.

Smithsonian Institution (US). 2011. *http://botany.si.edu/*, 2011-08-26.

The C. V. Starr Virtual Herbarium of The New York Botanical Garden (NY). 2010. *http://sciweb.nybg.org/science2/VirtualHerbarium.asp*, 2010-03-28.

Tropicos. 2010. Herbarium specimen data provided by: Institute for Botanical Exploration (IBE), Missouri Botanical Garden (MO), and University of Missouri (UMO). *http://www.tropicos.org/*, 2010-11-19.

University of Alaska Museum Herbarium (ALA). 2011. *http://arctos.database.museum/home.cfm*, 2011-01-12.

University of Alberta Vascular Plant Herbarium (ALTA). 2010. *http://vascularplant.museums.ualberta.ca*, 2010-12-03.

University of British Columbia Herbarium (UBC). 2010. Herbarium specimen data provided by personal communication. *http://www.biodiversity.ubc.ca/museum/herbarium/*, 2010-04-08.

University of Minnesota Herbarium / Bell Museum of Natural History (MIN). 2010. *www.bellmuseum.umn.edu*

University of Washington Herbarium (WTU). 2011. *http://www.washington.edu/burkemuseum/collections/herbarium/index.php*, 2011-01-07.

Robert Henszey, June, 2012
Fairbanks, Alaska

Ecoregions of Alaska

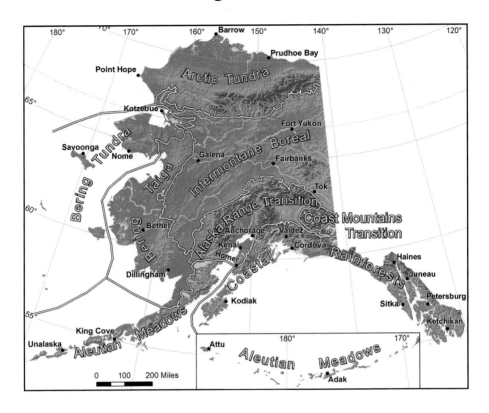

Aleutian Islands

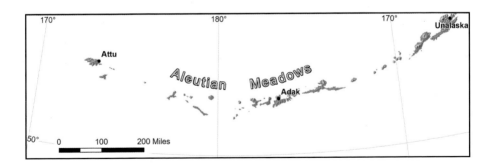

Level 2 Ecoregions of Alaska, representing a unified interagency effort to delineate ecoregion boundaries. After Nowacki et al. (2001) Ecoregions of Alaska, U.S. Geological Survey Open-File Report 02-297 (map), *http://agdc.usgs.gov/data/usgs/ecosafo/ecoreg/*.

Grass Plant

spikelets

spikelet

floret lemma

lemma awn

rachilla

palea

lemma awn

lemma

inflorescence

spikelets

1st or lower glume

2nd or upper glume

rachis lemma

florets

palea

lemma

rachis (stem within inflorescence to spikelets)

lemma awn

rachilla

culm (above ground and upright stem)

leaf blade

leaf collar

leaf sheath

rachis

1st glume

2nd glume

culm node

anthers

floret lemma

stigma

palea

basal leaves

filament

ovary

crown

stigma

callus

fibrous roots

style

ovary

lodicule

Plant Collar

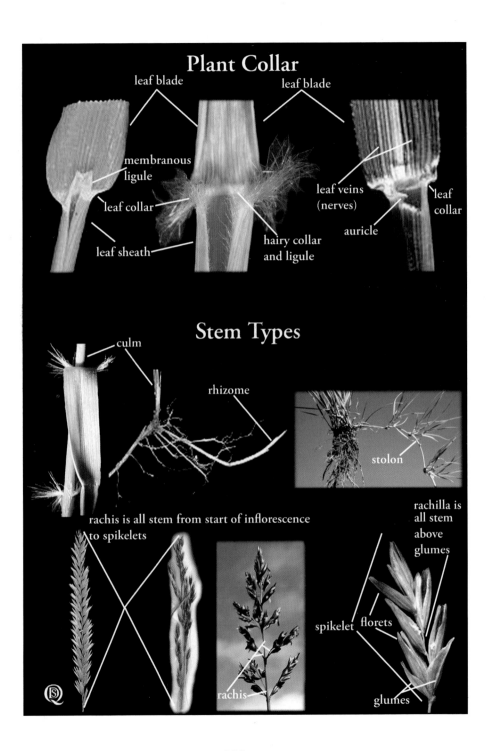

leaf blade

leaf blade

membranous ligule

leaf collar

leaf sheath

hairy collar and ligule

leaf veins (nerves)

auricle

leaf collar

Stem Types

culm

rhizome

stolon

rachis is all stem from start of inflorescence to spikelets

rachilla is all stem above glumes

spikelet   florets

rachis

glumes

XV

Inflorescence Types

Spike

spikelets lateral to the rachis
both glumes present

spikelets edgewise
to the rachis, one
glume missing

1 spikelet
per rachis
node

2 spikelets
per rachis
node

3 spikelets
per rachis
node

rachis

glume

Raceme

spikelets attached directly to a rachis or single rachis branch

rachis

rachis

spikelet

spikelets

Inflorescence Types Cont.

Panicle

cylindrical

compressed

spicate

dense spicate

appressed

open

diffuse

digital

Spikelet Types

multiple perfect florets; glumes longer than all lemmas

1 perfect soft floret; glumes longer than the lemma

multiple perfect florets; lower glume longer than the upper lemma, the upper glume longer than the lower lemmas

glumes shorter than the multiple florets within them; glumes and lemmas rounded on the back; spikelets relatively large

glumes shorter than the multiple florets within them; glumes and lemmas compressed

nerves of the lemmas parallel; upper glume 1-nerve

nerves of the lemmas parallel; upper glume 3-nerved

Spikelet Types Cont.

glumes · glumes · glumes · glumes · glumes

glumes shorter than the multiple florets within them; glumes and lemmas compressed; spikelets relatively large

glumes shorter than the multiple florets within them; glumes and lemmas compressed; spikelets relatively small

glumes shorter than the multiple florets within them, papery, and somewhat rounded on the back; spikelet size in between large and small

sterile florets

sterile florets

sterile floret

glumes longer than 1 fertile and 2 sterile florets

glumes subequal to 1 fertile and 2 sterile florets

1 glume as long or longer than 1 fertile and one sterile floret, the other shorter

Notes

TRIBES AND GENERA

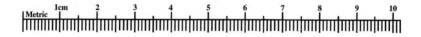

KEY TO THE GRASS TRIBES IN ALASKA

1. Inflorescence a spike
   2. Spikelets placed lateral to the rachis and both
      glumes present **TRITICEAE** p. 7
   2. Spikelets placed edgewise to the rachis and the
      upper glume missing **POEAE** (in part) p. 4
1. Inflorescence a panicle
   3. Ligule of hairs **DANTHONEAE** p. 7
   3. Ligule a membrane
      4. Spikelets 20-45 mm long; florets 2 or more; glumes firm; lemma
         nerves converging at the apex, upper lemmas exceeding both
         glumes, awned **BROMEAE** p.8
      4. Spikelets 1.4-28 mm long, florets 1-2 or more; glumes papery or firm; lemmas
         exceeding or included by glumes, lemma nerves parallel or converging at the
         apex, awned or awnless
         5. Spikelets 1.8-28 mm long; florets 2 or more; glumes papery, if firm the
            upper glume 1-nerved; upper lemmas exceeding both glumes, lemma
            nerves parallel **MELICEAE** p.4
         5. Spikelets 1.4-20 mm long; florets 1-2 or more; glumes firm; lemma
            nerves converging at the apex, if parallel the upper glume 3-7 nerved,
            upper lemmas exceeding or included by one or both glumes **POEAE** p. 4

KEY TO THE GENERA OF MELICEAE

1. Panicle nodes with 1 branch bearing a single spikelet; palea keels awned   *Pleuropogon sabinei* p. 28

1. Panicle nodes with 2 or more branches bearing 1-2 or more spikelets; palea keels awnless

   2. Glumes firm, upper glume 1-nerved; wet habitats   *Glyceria* p. 7 p. 32

   2. Glumes papery; upper glume 1-several nerved; dry habitats

      3. Callus hairy; lemmas awned   *Schizachne purpurascens* p. 30

      3. Callus glabrous; lemmas awnless   *Melica subulata* p. 44

KEY TO THE GENERA OF POEAE

1. Spikelets with a single floret

   2. Lemma exceeding at least 1 glume

      3. Glumes 1 mm or longer   *Arctagrostis* p. 9 p. 70

      3. Glumes minute, less than 1 mm long   *Phippsia algida* p. 74

   2. Lemma included within or subequal to both glumes

      4. Inflorescence a cylindrical panicle

        5. Glumes short awned; lemmas awnless   *Phleum* p. 9 p. 76

        5. Glumes awnless; lemmas awned   *Alopecurus* p. 9 p. 80

      4. Inflorescence an appressed, compressed, or open panicle

        6. Callus conspicuously hairy   *Calamagrostis* p. 9 p. 88

        6. Callus glabrous or only minutely hairy

          7. Floret and glumes disarticulating from a branch as one unit   *Cinna latifolia* p. 106

          7. Floret disarticulating from a branch alone leaving the glumes attached

            8. Palea well developed, at least half or more as long as the lemma, 2 nerves   *Podagrostis* p.10 p. 108

            8. Palea obsolete or usually less than half as long as the lemma, nerves absent   *Agrostis* p.10 p. 112

1. Spikelets with 2 or more florets

   9. Spikelets with a single perfect floret and 1 or more staminate or sterile florets

      10. Inflorescence a panicle of racemes; spikelets sessile to a rachis branch; glumes inflated or pyriform and includes all florets   *Beckmannia syzigachne* p. 128

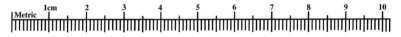

10. Inflorescence a panicle; spikelets from pedicels or branches; glumes
    not inflated or pyriform and includes all florets

   11. Spikelets with 3 florets, 2 sterile florets on each side of 1 perfect floret

      12. Sterile and perfect florets appearance similar   *Anthoxanthum* p. 11 p. 130

      12. Sterile florets short scale-like feathery appendages, the perfect
    glabrous and shiny   *Phalaris* p. 11 p. 138

   11. Spikelets with 2 florets, one sterile and the other perfect

      13. Sterile floret bearing a geniculate awn   *Arrhenatherum elatius* p. 142

      13. Sterile floret bearing a hooked awn   *Holcus lanatus* p. 144

9. Spikelets with 2 or more perfect florets, except ×*Duarctopoa* where all are sterile

   14. Lemmas included within the glumes, or the upper glume includes or is subequal
    to all lemmas and the lower glume only includes the lower or lowest lemmas

      15. Lemmas included within or subequal to both glumes

         16. Perennial; spikelets less than 1 cm long;
    lemmas keeled   *Vahlodea atropurpurea* p. 146

         16. Annual; spikelets greater than 1 cm long;
    lemmas rounded   *Avena* **p.** 11 p. 148

      15. Upper lemma exceeds the lower glume; the upper glume includes or is
    subequal to all lemmas

         17. Inflorescence a spike; spikelets placed edgewise to the rachis;
    first glume absent   *Lolium* p. 11 p. 152

         17. Inflorescence a panicle; spikelets on pedicels, both glumes present

            18. Lemmas awned, awns conspicuous

               19. Panicle open; spikelets shiny; lemma
    awns straight   *Deschampsia* p. 12 p. 156

               19. Panicle compressed to tightly appressed; spikelets not shiny;
    lemma awns strongly geniculate   *Trisetum* p.12 p. 166

            18. Lemmas awnless or awn tipped and awns not conspicuous

               20. Florets and glumes disarticulating from a branch
    as a single unit   *Sphenopholis intermedia* p. 172

               20. Florets disarticulating above the glumes leaving the glumes
    on the branch

                  21. Plants mostly tufted, panicle compressed; leaf sheaths open;
    leaves to 3 mm wide   *Koeleria asiatica* p. 174

21. Plants rhizomatous, panicles appressed to open; leaf sheaths closed ⅓-⅔ of their length; leaves 2-6 mm wide, flat

    22. Glumes subequal to longer than the lemmas within them; anthers and caryopsis present   *Dupontia* p. 12 p. 176

    22. Lower glume shorter than the lower lemma; upper glume subequal to the upper lemma; anthers indehiscent; caryopsis absent.   ×*Duarctopoa labradorica* p. 180

14. Lemmas generally exceed the glumes

  23. Lemma nerves converging toward the tip, not prominent, awned, acutely pointed, or awnless

    24. Spikelets crowded in 1-sided clusters at the ends of the naked panicle branches   *Dactylis glomerata* p. 182

    24. Spikelets evenly distributed on the panicle branches

      25. Lemma awned from the tip

        26. Blades flat, over 3 mm wide, leaf auricles present; awns less than 2 mm long   *Schedonorus* p. 13 p. 184

        26. Blades rolled or involute, less than 3 mm wide, leaf auricles absent; awns greater than 2 mm long   *Festuca* p. 13 p. 188

      25. Lemmas awnless

        27. Leaf blades soft; boat tipped   *Poa* p. 14 p. 218

        27. Leaf blades stiff; without boat tip   *Festuca* p. 13 p. 188

  23. Lemma nerves not converging near the apex, apex rounded, truncate, obtuse

    28. Spikelets 2 flowered, rarely 1-flowered   *Catabrosa aquatica* p. 282

    28. Spikelets several flowered

      29. Sheaths closed for more than ½ their length   *Arctophila fulva* p. 284

      29. Sheaths open

        30. Culms stout; strongly rhizomatous; upper glume 3-7 nerved; lemma nerves excurrent; apices 3-lobed   *Scolochloa festucacea* p. 286

        30. Culms slender; rhizomatous or tufted; upper glume 3 nerved; lemma nerves not excurrent,

          31. Lemma nerves prominent, raised; ligules over 3 mm long   *Torreyochloa pallida* var. *pauciflora* p. 288

          31. Lemma nerves faint; ligules to 3 mm long   *Puccinellia* p. 17 p. 290

KEY TO THE GENERA OF TRITICEAE

1. Spikelets 3 at each node, the central spikelet sessile, the lateral spikelets pedicelled; 1-flowered   *Hordeum* p. 19 p. 314

1. Spikelets 1-several at each node, all sessile; 2-many flowered

   2. Plants annual

      3. Spikes broad; glumes ovate, 3-to many-nerved; lemmas awnless or awns of variable length   *Triticum aestivum* p. 324

      3. Spikes narrow; glumes linear to subulate, 1-nerved; lemma long awned   *Secale cereale* p. 326

   2. Plants perennial

      4. Spikelets 1 at each rachis node, closely imbricate, generally pectinate when mature   *Agropyron cristatum* p. 328

      4. Spikelets usually 2 or more at some rachis nodes, if 1 then not closely imbricate nor pectinate

         5. Glumes broadest near base, keels lying to one side of keels of the lowest lemmas   *Leymus* p. 19 p. 330

         5. Glumes broader to broadest above the base, keels in line with keels of the lowest lemmas

            6. Spikelets 1 at the rachis nodes   *Elymus* p. 19 p. 336
            6. Spikelets 2 or more spikelets at the rachis nodes   *Elymus* p. 20 p. 350

KEY TO THE SPECIES OF DANTHONIA

1. Lemma back glabrous, densely pilose only along margins   *D. intermedia* p. 24
1. Lemma back pilose, pilose only to the middle of margins   *D. spicata* p. 26

KEY TO THE SPECIES OF GLYCERIA

1. Panicles narrow, erect with appressed branches; spikelets linear

   2. Lemmas glabrous on nerve keels   *G. borealis* p. 32

   2. Lemmas scabrous on nerve keels, also between nerves   *G. leptostachya* p. 34

1. Panicles open with spreading and often nodding branches; spikelets ovate or oblong

   3. First glumes 0.6-1.5 mm long; spikelets 1.8-4 mm long   *G. striata* p. 36

   3. First glumes 1-3 mm long; spikelets 3-10 mm long

      4. Upper glumes 3-5 mm long   *G. maxima* p. 38

      4. Upper glumes 1.5-2.7 mm long

         5. Plants stout, culms 8-12 mm thick; branch spikelets 30-80+, 3-10 mm long; lemma apex entire   *G. grandis* p. 40

KEY TO THE SPECIES OF GLYCERA CONT.

5. Plants slender, culms 1.5-5 mm thick; branch spikelets
   30-40+, 3.5-6 mm long; lemma apex erose ..... *G. pulchella* p. 42

KEY TO THE SPECIES OF BROMUS

1. Plants annual
   - 2. Lower glumes 1-3-veined; upper glume 3-5-veined ..... *B. tectorum* p. 46
   - 2. Lower glumes 3-5-veined; upper glume 5-9-veined
     - 3. Panicle branches shorter than the spikelets ..... *B. hordeaceus* p. 48
     - 3. Panicle branches longer than the spikelets ..... *B. secalinus* p. 50
1. Plants perennial
   - 4. Spikelets strongly flattened; lemmas compressed-keeled
     - 5. Lower panicle branches greater than 10 cm long ..... *B. sitchensis* p. 52
     - 5. Lower panicle branches less than 10 cm long
       - 6. Culms greater than 3 mm thick ..... *B. aleutensis* p. 54
       - 6. Culms less than 3 mm thick ..... *B. carinatus* var. *marginatus* p. 56
   - 4. Spikelets little flattened; lemmas mostly rounded on the back
     - 7. Plants rhizomatous; lemmas awnless or awned
       - 8. Lemmas awnless or if awned, awns to 3 mm long, mostly glabrous ..... *B. inermis* p. 58
       - 8. Lemmas awned, awns to 7.5 mm long, sparsely to densely pubescenct
         - 9. Plants with few culms together ..... *B. pumpellianus* subsp. *pumpellianus* p. 60
         - 9. Plants with many culms together, tufted ..... *B. pumpellianus* subsp. *dicksonii* p. 62
     - 7. Plants tufted; rhizomes lacking; lemma awned, 2-10 mm long
       - 10. Glumes pubescent, rarely glabrous; ligules 2-4 mm long; anthers 2-4 mm long ..... *B. pacificus* p. 64
       - 10. Glumes usually glabrous; ligules 0.4-2 mm long; anthers 1-2.7
         - 11. Lemmas glabrous; anthers 1-1.4 mm long ..... *B. ciliatus* p. 66
         - 11. Upper lemmas pubescent; anthers 1.6-2.7 mm long ..... *B. richardsonii* p. 68

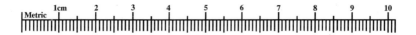

KEY TO THE SPECIES OF ARCTAGROSTIS

1. Culms 5-15 dm tall; panicles open and large, longest
    branches 3-27 cm long   *A. latifolia* subsp. *arundinacea* p. 70

1. Culms 1.5-5 dm tall; panicles contracted;
    longest branches 0.5-4 cm long   *A. latifolia* subsp. *latifolia* p. 72

KEY TO THE SPECIES OF PHLEUM

1. Culms over 5 dm tall, erect from a swollen bulblike base; panicle
    narrow and long, greater than 4 times as long as wide   *P. pratense* p. 76

1. Culms 2-5 dm tall, erect from a decumbent creeping slender base;
    panicle narrow and short, not more than 4 times as long as wide   *P. alpinum* p. 78

KEY TO THE SPECIES OF ALOPECURUS

1. Spikelets 4-6 mm long   *A. pratensis* p. 80

1. Spikelets 2-4 mm long

    2. Panicle oblong or ovoid, about 1 cm wide; glumes
        densely woolly or villous all over   *A. magellanicus* p. 82

    2. Panicle oblong or ovoid, less than 1 cm wide; glumes
        villous on keel and nerves only

        3. Awn exceeding the glumes by 1.5 mm or less   *A. aequalis* p. 84

        3. Awn exceeding the glumes by more than 2 mm   *A. geniculatus* p. 86

KEY TO THE SPECIES OF CALAMAGROSTIS

1. Lemma awns exserted, awn distinct within callus hairs, distinctly bent, twisted, or
    geniculate

    2. Plants loosely tufted to rhizomatous   *C. deschampsioides* p. 88

    2. Plants strongly tufted

        3. Awn usually 4.5-9 mm long; leaf blades densely hairy on the
            adaxial surface   *C. purpurascens* p. 90

        3. Awn usually 7-11 mm long; leaf blades usually slightly scabrous to
            glabrous and sparsely hairy on the adaxial surface   *C. sesquiflora* p. 92

1. Lemma awns not exserted or if so barely, awn delicate or stout, hidden or
    distinct within callus hairs, straight to slightly bent or twisted

    4. Culms stout, 3-4 mm thick; lemmas 4-5 mm long   *C. nutkaensis* p. 94

    4. Culms slender, less than 3 mm thick; lemmas 2-4 mm long

        5. Panicle loose and open at anthesis; branches 2.7-12 cm long; callus hairs the
            same length, longer than the lemma; lemma awn delicate and straight

KEY TO THE SPECIES OF CALAMAGROSTIS CONT.

    6.   Spikelets 4-4.5 mm long; glumes distinctly acuminate, scabrous on the keels and elsewhere; awn inconspicuous and delicate   *C. canadensis* var. *langsdorffii* p. 96

    6.   Spikelets 2.5-4 mm long; glume apices acute, somewhat rounded, smooth or scabrous only on the keels; lemma awn slender, sometimes twisted   *C. canadensis* var. *canadensis* p. 98

5.   Panicle tightly appressed to contracted; branches 1.4-9.5 cm long; callus hairs of mixed length, the longest subequal to the lemma; lemma awn delicate or stout, straight

    7.   Glume length usually more than 3 times the width; spikelets 3.5-5.5 mm long; lemma awns delicate and similar to callus hairs   *C. lapponica* p. 100

    7.   Glume length less than 3 times the width; spikelets 2-5 mm long; lemma awns stout, distinct from callus hairs

        8.   Spikelets 3-5 mm long; callus hairs 2-4.5 mm long; rachilla prolongations 1-1.5 mm long; panicle branches 1.5-9.5 cm long   *C. stricta* subsp. *inexpansa* p. 102

        8.   Spikelets 2-3 mm long; callus hairs 1-3 mm long; rachilla prolongations 0.5-1 mm long; panicle branches 1.4-4 cm long   *C. stricta* subsp. *stricta* p. 104

KEY TO THE SPECIES OF PODAGROSTIS

1.   Spikelets 2.3-4.3 mm long; rachilla prolongation 0.5-1.9 mm   *P. aequivalvis* p. 108

1.   Spikelets 1.6-2.3 mm long; rachilla prolongation 0.1-0.6 mm   *P. humilis* p.110

KEY TO THE SPECIES OF AGROSTIS

1.   Plants stoloniferous or rhizomatous; paleas over $^2/_5$ the length of the lemma

    2.   Plants stoloniferous; panicle branches floriferous to the base   *A. stolonifera* p. 112

    2.   Plants rhizomatous

        3.   Panicle branches floriferous to the base   *A. gigantea* p.114

        3.   Panicle branches naked at base   *A. capillaris* p. 116

1.   Plants tufted, rhizomes present or absent; paleas absent or less than $^2/_5$ the length of the lemma

    4.   Panicles narrow, contracted, branches floriferous to the base   *A. exarata* p. 118

    4.   Panicles open, branches naked near the base

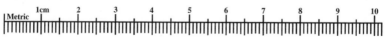

10

KEY TO THE SPECIES OF AGROSTIS CONT.

5. Lemmas with prominent geniculate awn from below the middle, exserted from the glumes

   6. Anthers 0.5-0.8 mm long; panicle appressed to contracted   *A. mertensii* p. 120

   6. Anthers 0.7-1.8 mm long; panicle open   *A. vinealis* p. 122

5. Lemmas awnless or the awn short, straight, seldom exserted from the glumes

   7. Plants perennial; lemmas ½ to ⅔ as long as the glumes; awned or awnless, when awned the length and degree of bend varies; leaf blades to 2 mm wide   A. *scabra* p. 124

   7. Plants annual or short-lived perennial; lemmas subequal to the glumes, awnless; leaf blades to 7 mm wide   *A. clavata* p. 126

KEY TO THE SPECIES OF ANTHOXANTHUM

1. Glumes unequal, lower glume shorter; lower 2 florets sterile   *A. odoratum* p. 130

1. Glumes subequal; lower florets staminate

   2. Plants tufted; staminate florets distinctly awned   *A. monticola* subsp. *alpinum* p. 132

   2. Plants rhizomatous; lemmas awnless to pointed

      3. Panicle linear or spikelike; 1-2 spikelets per short (to 1 cm long) branches   *A. arcticum* p. 134

      3. Panicle not linear or spikelike; generally 3 or more spikelets per longer (to 5 cm long) branches   *A. hirtum* p. 136

KEY TO THE SPECIES OF PHALARIS

1. Plants perennial, culms over 6 dm tall; panicle narrow but not spikelike   *P. arundinacea* p. 138

1. Plants annual, culms less than 6 dm tall; panicle dense and spikelike   *P. canariensis* p.140

KEY TO THE SPECIES OF AVENA

1. Spikelets 2-flowered, the florets not readily separating; awns straight or absent; lemmas glabrous   *A. sativa* p. 148

1. Spikelets 3-flowered, the florets readily separating; awns stout, geniculate, twisted; lemmas with stiff brown hairs   *A. fatua* p.150

KEY TO THE SPECIES OF LOLIUM

1. Plants perennial; lemmas awnless or sometimes awned   *L. perenne* p. 152

1. Plants annual or short-lived perennials; lemmas awned   *L. multiflorum* p. 154

KEY TO THE SPECIES OF DESCHAMPSIA

1. Panicles narrowly elongate, more than ¼ the length of the culm, the distant branches appressed; awns to twice as long as florets   *D. elongata* p. 156

1. Panicles open or contracted, if narrow not more than ¼ the length of the culms; awns subequal to just longer than the florets

    2. Panicles appressed to contracted; spikelets overlapping each other along or in clusters on end of branches; glumes purple   *D. brevifolia* p. 158

    2. Panicles open; spikelets not overlapping along or on the ends of branches; glumes less than half purple

        3. Plants less than 3 dm tall; new year leaves capillary, strongly involute, less than 0.5 mm wide, 3-5 nerves; lower glumes smooth over the midnerve   *D. sukatschewii* p. 160

        3. Plants over 3 dm tall; new year leaves 1-4 mm wide, flat to involute, 5-11 nerves; lower glumes often scabridulous distally over the midnerve

            4. Glumes narrow, lanceolate, 5-7 mm long; awns conspicuously exceeding the lemmas   *D. cespitosa* subsp. *beringensis* p. 162

            4 Glumes broader compared to length, 2-6 mm long; awns subequal or exceeded by the lemmas   *D. cespitosa* subsp. *cespitosa* p. 164

KEY TO THE SPECIES OF TRISETUM

1. Plants rhizomatous; culms usually solitary; panicles ovoid or broadly spikelike   *T. sibiricum* p. 166

1. Plants tufted, not rhizomatous; panicles spikelike or open

    2. Panicles spikelike; spikelets in fascicles; glumes subequal   *T. spicatum* p. 168

    2. Panicle open, drooping; spikelet-bearing at branch apices; glumes unequal   *T. cernuum* p. 170

KEY TO THE SPECIES OF DUPONTIA

1. Plants less than 3 dm tall; glumes blunt; lemmas subsericeous   *D. fisheri* subsp. *fisheri* p. 176

1. Plants over 3 dm tall; glumes long-acuminate; lemmas glabrous   *D. fisheri* subsp. *psilosantha* p. 178

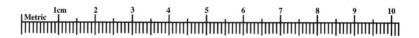

KEY TO THE SPECIES OF SCHEDONORUS

1. Leaf auricles ciliate; panicles open and nodding; lemmas more than 8 mm long   *S. arundinaceus* p. 184

1. Leaf auricles glabrous; panicles appressed to open; lemmas less than 8 mm long   *S. pratensis* p. 186

KEY TO THE SPECIES OF FESTUCA

1. Blades flat, lax, more than 3 mm wide   *F. subulata* p. 188

1. Blades folded, involute or if flat less than 3 mm wide

   2. Plants rhizomatous

      3. Lemmas pilose, awns to 1.6 mm long   *F. rubra* subsp. *arctica* p. 190

      3. Lemmas glabrous, awns longer than 1.6. mm

         4. Mature inflorescence partly included in the uppermost sheaths; cauline leaves 2-4 mm wide, usually open   *F. rubra* subsp. *aucta* p. 192

         4. Mature inflorescence exserted from the sheaths; cauline leaves less than 2 mm wide, usually folded

            5. Lower glumes 3-4.5 mm long; inflorescence 7-12 cm long   *F. rubra* subsp. *rubra* p. 194

            5. Lower glumes 2.2-3.2 mm long; inflorescence 3-10 cm long   *F. rubra* subsp. *pruinosa* p. 196

   2. Plants tufted

      6. Plants pseudoviviparous   *F. viviparoidea* p. 198

      6. Plants not pseudoviviparous

         7. Plants tall, culms usually over 4 dm tall; panicles open, lax, often secund, drooping or reflexed

            8. Lemma awns 0.2-0.7 mm long   *F. altaica* p. 200

            8. Lemma awns 3-12 mm long   *F. occidentalis* p. 202

         7. Plants shorter, culms usually less than 4 dm tall; panicles narrow, appressed to compressed

            9. Anthers 2-3.5 mm long   *F. lenensis* p. 204

            9. Anthers less than 2 mm long

               10. Culms densely tomentose on the upper half   *F. baffinensis* p. 206

               10. Culms glabrous or scabrous on the upper half

                  11. Plants to 4 dm tall; inflorescence usually greater than 5 cm long; anthers 1.2-1.7 mm long   *F. saximontana* p. 208

13

KEY TO THE SPECIES OF FESTUCA CONT.

11. Plants shorter, to 3 dm tall; inflorescence to 4 cm long; anthers 0.6-1.2 mm long

    12. Sheaths of the flag leaf not inflated   *F. brachyphylla* p. 210

    12. Sheaths of the flag leaf distinctly to somewhat inflated

        13. Foliage fine and bristlelike; lemmas 2.2-3.5 mm long; inflorescence a panicle of multiple branches   *F. minutiflora* p. 212

        13. Foliage various, but not fine and bristlelike; lemmas 3-7 mm long; inflorescence a panicle with single branches

            14. Culms erect, over 2 times the height of the basal tuft of leaves   *F. brevissima* p. 214

            14. Culms usually geniculate to prostrate, to 2 times the height if the basal tuft of leaves   *F. edlundiae* p. 216

KEY TO THE SPECIES OF POA

1. Plants annual   *P. annua* p. 218

1. Plants perennial

    2. Spikelets dorsally compressed, mostly rounded; length 3-5 times longer than wide; lemmas rounded to faintly keeled on the back

        3. Plants densely to loosely tufted; culms often decumbent; anthers 2-2.8 mm long; high arctic species   *P. hartzii* subsp. *alaskana* p. 220

        3. Plants densely tufted; culms upright; anthers 1.5-3 mm long; not a high arctic species

            4. Lemmas glabrous; keel obscure   *P. secunda* subsp. *juncifolia* p. 222

            4. Lemmas pubescent, keels obscure or faintly present

                5. Lemma keels obscure to faintly present, hairs less than 0.5 mm long   *P. secunda* subsp. *secunda* p. 224

                5. Lemma keels faintly present, hairs of keels and nerves prevalent, longer than 0.5 mm   *P. stenantha* p. 226

    2. Spikelets distinctly laterally compressed, length to 3 times longer than wide; lemmas keeled to the base

        6. Culms conspicuously flattened   *P. compressa* p. 228

        6. Culms slightly compressed to round

14

KEY TO THE SPECIES OF POA CONT.

7. Anthers usually 1.1 mm or longer

  8. Callus hairy or webbed, sometimes scantily so

   9. Lemmas glabrous or pubescent, lacking long or lanate hairs between the keel and nerves

    10. Plants distinctly rhizomatous

     11. Culms usually solitary, thick (to 2 mm); leaves 5-10 mm wide; panicle branch spikelet bearing to the base; callus with a crown of hairs   *P. eminens* p. 230

     11. Culms more prevalent to loosely tufted, slender; leaves less than 5 mm wide; panicle branch spikelet bearing above the base; callus webbed

      12. Spikelets mostly 2 florets; glumes subequal to just shorter than the lemmas   *P. macrocalyx* p. 232

      12. Spikelets more than 2 florets; glumes distinctly shorter than upper lemmas of the spikelets

       13 Panicles 14-30 cm long, open, lax, branches 2-15 cm long, 2-3 per lower nodes; spikelets to 1.1 mm long   *P. laxiflora* p. 234

       13 Panicles 2-9 cm long, appressed to open, branches 8-12 cm long, 2-7 branches per lower nodes; spikelets >1.1 mm long

        14. Vivipary present; plants of the high arctic   *P. pratensis* subsp. *colpodea* p. 236

        14. Vivipary absent; plants of a wide distribution

         15. Panicle branches smooth   *P. pratensis* subsp. *alpigena* p. 238

         15. Panicle branches scabrous

          16. Leaves firm, folded to involute, 0.4-1 mm wide   *P. pratensis* subsp. *angustifolia* p. 240

          16. Leaves softer, flat to folded, 1.5-4.5 mm wide

           17. Culms to 10 dm high, usually green; panicle branches 3-5   *P. pratensis* subsp. **pratensis** p. 242

           17. Culms to 5 dm high; often glaucous; panicle branches usually only 1-2   *P. pratensis* subsp. *irrigata* p. 244

    10. Plants tufted

     18. First glume narrow and curved, acute; lemmas with a distinct nerve between the keel and marginal nerve   *P. trivialis* p. 246

KEY TO THE SPECIES OF POA CONT.

18. First glume narrow or broader; lemmas without a distinct nerve between the keel and marginal nerve

    19. Culms with 1 node at about ⅓ its length; plants usually glaucous

        20. Callus webbed; lemmas either glabrous or hairy between the veins   *P. glauca* subsp. *glauca* p. 248

        20. Callus glabrous; lemmas hairy between the veins   *P. glauca* subsp. *rupicola* p. 250

    19. Culms with 2 or more nodes; usually not glaucous

        21. Nodes 2, highest between ⅓-⅔ its length   *P. interior* p. 252

        21. Nodes 3-5, extended to higher on the culm

            22. Densely tufted; ligules 0.2-0.8 mm long   *P. nemoralis* p. 254

            22. Loosely tufted; ligules 1.5-6 mm long   *P. palustris* p. 256

9. Lemmas with long or lanate hairs between the keel and basal part of the marginal nerve

    23. Panicle nodding; spikelets green to part violet, 6-9 mm long   *P. macrocalyx* p. 232

    23. Panicle erect; spikelets mostly violet, 4-17 mm long

        24. Culms stout, 1.5-2 mm thick; spikelets 6-17 mm long; palea glabrous between keel and marginal nerves; rhizomes thick, to 4 m long   *P. macrantha* p. 258

        24. Culms normal to slender; spikelets 4-8 mm long; palea pubescent between the keel and marginal nerves; rhizomes thin subterranean runners

            25. Lemma area between the keels and marginal nerves completely covered by hairs; keel and marginal nerves densely hairy showing a cotton appearance   *P. sublanata* p. 260

            25. Lemma area between the keels and marginal nerves hairy but not dense, sometimes nearly glabrous

                26. Rhizomes not well developed, plants loosely tufted; high arctic distribution   *P. arctica* subsp. *caespitans* p. 262

                26. Rhizomes well developed subterranean runners, short to long, culms solitary or a few culms at a single location, broad distribution

                    27. Spikelets 6-8 mm long; rachillas usually hairy   *P. arctica* subsp. *lanata* p. 264

KEY TO THE SPECIES OF POA CONT.

    27. Spikelets 4.5-6 mm long; rachillas usually
glabrous   *P. arctica* subsp. *arctica* p. 266

  8. Callus not webbed at the base

    28. Lemmas glabrous; interior and high mountains   *P. porsildii* p. 268

    28. Lemmas villous to pubescent on the keel, marginal nerves, or both, and
sometimes on the internerves as well

      29. Panicle about as wide as long; spikelets broad, subcordate;
leaves broad and relatively short   *P. alpina* p. 270

      29. Panicles longer than wide; spikelets long, narrow,
acute; leaves narrow and longer   *P. stenantha* p. 226

  7. Anthers usually less than 1.1 mm long

    30. Lower panicle branches single or in pairs, spreading, drooping, or reflexed;
callus distinctly webbed

      31. Culms to 3 dm tall; panicles 2.5-10 cm long;
branches smooth; spikelets ovate   *P. paucispicula* p. 272

      31. Culms 1.5-10 dm tall; panicles 5-15 cm
long; branches scabrous; spikelets narrow   *P. leptocoma* p. 274

    30. Lower panicle branches 1-3 per node; panicle shape compressed, rhomboidal, or
pyramidal, branches usually not reflexed; callus glabrous or sometimes webbed

      32. Panicle rhomboidal or pyramidal, branches longer, somewhat capillary,
and spreading; callus web lacking; lemmas puberulent on the keels and
marginal veins only   *P. pseudoabbreviata* p.276

      32. Panicle compressed, branches short, somewhat stiff, ascending; callus
glabrous or webbed; lemmas villous to puberulent on the keels, marginal
nerves, and glabrous to soft-puberulent or villous in between

        33. Callus usually glabrous; lemma vein intercostal regions softly
puberulent to short-villous; anthers
0.2-0.8 mm long   *P. abbreviata* subsp. *abbreviata* p. 278

        33. Callus usually webbed; lemma vein intercostal regions
glabrous or softly puberulent; anthers
0.6-1.2 mm long   *P. abbreviata* subsp. *pattersonii* p. 280

KEY TO THE SPECIES OF PUCCINELLIA

1. Plants stoloniferous, forming mats along the ocean tideline;
inflorescence mostly lacking   *P. phryganodes* p. 290

1. Plants perennial, but not mat forming; sexually reproducing

17

KEY TO THE SPECIES OF PUCCINELLIA CONT.

2. Palea nerves with curly, intertwined hairs near the base, scabrous near the apex

   3. Pedicels scabrous; apical margins of the lemma scabrous, nerves obscure   *P. angustata* p. 292

   3. Pedicels smooth; apical margins of the lemma smooth, nerves distinct or obscure

      4. Plants shorter, 5-15 cm tall; anthers 0.8-1.5 mm long   *P. vahliana* p. 294

      4. Plants taller, 15-40 cm tall; anthers 1.5-2.5 mm long   *P. wrightii* p. 296

2. Palea nerves glabrous at the base of the palea, sometimes short hairs or a few long hairs, may be scabrous near the apex

   5. Lemma margins smooth, may be a few scabrules near the tip

      6. Lemmas 2-2.5 mm long, nerves distinct, mostly purple with white margins; anthers 0.6-0.9 mm long   *P. tenella* p. 298

      6. Lemmas 2.4-4.6 mm long, nerves obscure or distinct, margins variously colored, not white; anthers 0.5-2.2 mm long

         7. Lemmas glabrous to a few hairs on the lower part of nerves; lemma tips entire; anthers 0.5-1.2 mm long   *P. pumila* p. 300

         7. Lemmas somewhat hairy on the lower part of nerves; lemma tips entire, serrate, or erose; anthers 0.8-2.2 mm long

            8. Panicle branches usually more than 2 at lowest node; lemma nerves obscure to distinct, margins often inrolled, tips entire to slightly erose; anthers 1.2-2.2 mm long   *P. arctica* p. 302

            8. Panicle branches usually 2 at lowest node; lemma nerves obscure, margins not inrolled, tips serrate or erose; anthers 0.8-1.2 mm long   *P. andersonii* p. 304

   5. Lemma margins distinctly scabrous near the tip

      9. Lemmas 1.5-2 mm long, tip obtuse to truncate; anthers 0.4-0.8 mm long; lower panicle branches reflexed at maturity   *P. distans* p. 306

      9. Lemmas 2.2-5 mm long, tip usually acute to obtuse; anthers 0.5-2 mm long; lower panicle branches stiffly ascending to somewhat reflexed at maturity

         10. Plants short, culms 0.9-2 dm tall; lower glumes 1.3-2.1 mm long; panicles diffuse to contracted, barely exserted from the sheath; anthers 0.7-1.2 mm long   *P. vaginata* p. 308

KEY TO THE SPECIES OF PUCCINELLIA CONT.

10. Plants taller, culms 1.0-10 dm tall; lower glumes 0.5-1.6 mm long; panicles appressed to open, exserted from the sheath; anthers 0.5-2 mm long

    11. Pedicels often swollen, not uniformly scabrous; panicles usually erect and appressed; lower glume 1-1.6 mm long; lemmas usually 3-4.5 mm long; anthers 0.5-1.4 mm long   *P. nutkaensis* p. 310

    11. Pedicels normal, uniformly scabrous; panicles open and lower branches often reflexed; lower glume 0.5-1.5 mm long; lemmas usually 2.2-3 mm long; anthers 0.6-2 mm long   *P. nuttalliana* p. 312

KEY TO THE SPECIES OF HORDEUM

1. Plants perennial

    2. Spike 3-15 cm, wide, glume awns 35-85 mm long *H. jubatum (jubatum)* p. 314

    2. Spike narrower, glume awns 7-35 mm long

        3. Glume awns flexuous, 15-35 mm long   *H. jubatum (intermedium)* p. 316

        3. Glume awns stiff, 7-17 mm long   *H. brachyantherum* p. 318

1. Plants annual

    4. Plants 10 to 15 dm tall; spikes exserted from the upper sheath; rachis continuous, the 3 spikelets sessile, 1 to all fertile; central spikelet pubescent; lemmas 3 mm or more wide   *H. vulgare* p. 320

    4. Plants to 11 dm tall, usually shorter; spike partially enclosed by the upper sheath; rachis disarticulating; central spikelet sessile, fertile, ciliate, lateral spikelets pedicellate and staminate; lemmas to 2 mm wide   *H. murinum* subsp. *leporinum* p. 322

KEY TO THE SPECIES OF LEYMUS

1. Glumes keeled distally, subulate; lemmas awns 2-4 mm long; plants not glaucous; rhizomes less than 2 mm thick   *L. innovatus* subsp. *velutinus* p. 330

1. Glumes flat, rounded on the back, lanceolate; lemmas awnless; plants often glaucous; rhizomes 2-6 mm thick

    2. Culms to 17 dm tall; rhizomes 4-6 mm thick; spikes 12-34 cm long, 12-33 nodes; blades 5-15 mm wide   *L. mollis* subsp. *mollis* p. 332

    2. Culms to 7 dm tall; rhizomes about 2 mm thick; spikes to 13 cm long, 3-14 nodes; blades 3-8 mm wide   *L. mollis* subsp. *villosissimus* p. 334

KEY TO THE SPECIES OF ELYMUS

1. Spikelet 1 at a rachis node

    2. Plants distinctly rhizomatous; anthers 4-7 mm long   *E. repens* p. 336

KEY TO THE SPECIES OF ELYMUS CONT.

2. Plants tufted to sometimes weakly rhizomatous; anthers 0.7-3 mm long

   3. Lemma awn longer than body, 17-40 mm long, straight; spikes
somewhat 1-sided   *E. trachycaulus* subsp. ***subsecundus*** p. 338

   3. Lemma awn absent to variable, straight; spikes 2-sided

      4. Glumes ⅓-⅔ as long as adjacent lemmas; lemma awns less than 8 mm long

         5. Glumes lanceolate, 0.8-1.8 mm wide, margins subequal;
lemmas evenly hairy or glabrous near the tip   *E. macrourus* p. 340

         5. Glumes oblanceolate to obovate, 1.5-2 mm wide, margins unequal;
lemmas glabrous to more densely hairy near the tip

            6. Glumes and lemmas densely
hairy   *E. alaskanus* subsp. ***hyperarcticus*** p. 342

            6. Glumes glabrous; lemmas somewhat
hairy towards the tips   *E. alaskanus* subsp. ***alaskanus*** p. 344

      4. Glumes ¾ as long or just longer than the adjacent lemmas; lemma awns
0.5-24 mm long

         7. Glumes usually 3 nerved, margins unequal, widest near
the tip; lemma awns 0.5-3 mm long   *E. violaceus* p. 346

         7. Glumes 3-7 nerved, margins subequal; lemma awns absent
to 5 mm long   *E. trachycaulus* subsp. ***trachycaulus*** p. 348

1. Spikelets usually 2 at a rachis node

  8. Anthers 0.9-1.7 mm long; spikes usually pendent   *E. sibiricus* p. 350

  8. Anthers 1.5-4 mm long; spikes usually upright, may be nodding when mature

    9. Glume bodies 7-10 mm long; auricles often absent or to 1.5 mm long; spikes
nodding to pendent; lemma awns often curving outward   *E. hirsutus* p. 352

    9. Glume bodies 9-14 mm long; auricles usually present to 2.5 mm long; spikes
mostly upright to nodding; lemma awns usually straight

      10. Lemma awns 1-5 mm long; glume
awns 0-2 mm long   *E. glaucus* subsp. ***virescens*** p. 354

      10. Lemma awns 10-25 mm long; glume
awns 1-5 mm long   *E. glaucus* subsp. ***glaucus*** p. 356

Notes

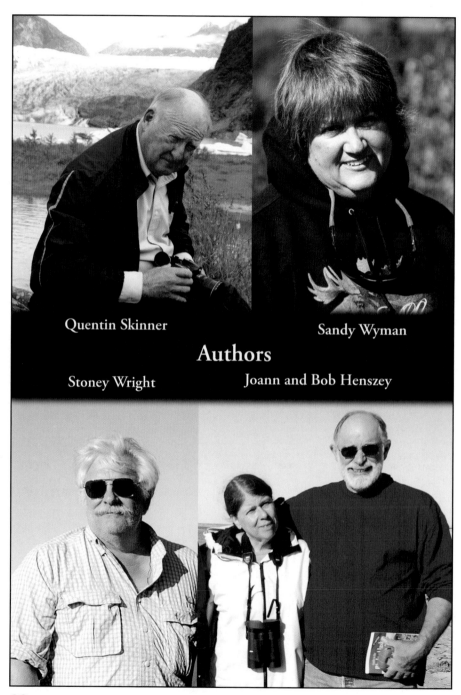

Quentin Skinner

Sandy Wyman

Authors

Stoney Wright

Joann and Bob Henszey

23

Timber oatgrass
Danthonia intermedia Vasey

Perennial, tufted; appressed-panicle inflorescence; ligule hairy; glumes 2, at least as, or longer than, the lowest floret, about 15 mm long; perfect florets 2 or more; lemma tip 3-lobed, the middle lobe often produced into a geniculate awn 6.5-8 mm long, glabrous over the back, pilose along margins and on callus only, 7-8 mm long.

Plants perennial, tufted; culms 1.3-5.1 dm tall, hollow, smooth, glabrous; vernation folded; sheaths open, smooth, glabrous or sparsely pilose; blades 5-10 cm long, 1-3.5 mm wide, flat or involute, glabrous or somewhat pilose; collars pilose, yellow; auricles absent; ligules hairy, 0.2-1 mm long.

Panicle purplish, narrow, few-flowered, 2-5 cm long, the branches appressed, bearing a single spikelet; spikelets 3-6 flowered; glumes about 15 mm long; lemmas 7-8 mm long, appressed pilose along the margin below and on the callus, the summit scaberulous, the teeth acuminate; terminal segment of awn 6.5-8 mm long; palea narrowed above, notched at the apex.

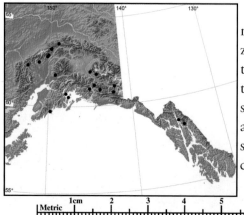

Native grass common to moist mountain meadow riparian zones. Often found above timberline on hummocks above the summer water table . A late seral riparian zone species when associated with mature streambanks and well-drained conditions.

Timber oatgrass
Tribe: Danthonieae

appressed panicle
spikelets

geniculate and
twisted awns

multiple
florets

spikelet

florets

lemma

palea

long
glumes

ligule

Poverty oatgrass
Danthonia spicata (L.) P. Beauv. *ex* Roem. & Schult.

Perennial, tufted; appressed-panicle inflorescence; ligule hairy; glumes 2, at least as, or longer than, the lowest floret, 10-13 mm long; perfect florets 2 or more; lemma tip 3-lobed, the middle lobe often produced into a geniculate awn, sparsely to densely pilose over the back, 4-7 mm long.

Plants perennial, tufted; culms 2-7 dm tall, hollow, smooth or scaberulous, glabrous, or puberulent below nodes; vernation folded, sheaths open, smooth, pilose; blades 6-15 cm long, up to 2 mm wide, flat or involute, pilose below, smooth or scabrous above; collars pilose, yellowish, interrupted; auricles absent; ligules hairy, 0.2-0.5 mm long.

Panicle 2-4 cm long, contracted, the short branches erect or ascending with mostly 2 spikelets; spikelets several flowered; glumes subequal, 10-13 mm long, oblong-lanceolate, acuminate; lemmas 4-7 mm long including the apical teeth, pubescent or villous on the back; awn flat, twisted and divergent, 6-10 mm long.

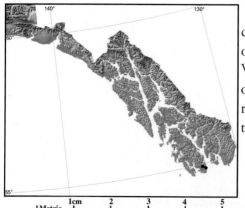

Rare in Alaska where collections have only occurred on drier rocky slopes of Prince of Wales Island. Generally found on dry well drained soils in open rocky pine forests and margins in the lower 48 states.

Poverty oatgrass
Tribe: Danthonieae

spikelets

florets

upper glume

lower glume

appressed panicle inflorescence

twisted and geniculate awns

floret lemma

floret palea

florets

hairy ligule and collar

27

False semaphoregrass
Pleuropogon sabinei R. Br.

Perennial, rhizomatous; one sided open panicle with 1 branch and spikelet per node; ligule membranous; spikelet relatively small with several florets; glumes papery and shorter than the florets within them; lemma veins parallel and not converging near the tip; palea keels each with 2 awns.

Plants perennial, rhizomatous and not caespitose; culms to 3.5 dm tall, 1-3 mm thick; ligules membranous, 1-3 mm long; leaf blades flat, 1-3 mm wide and to 5 dm long, often floating.

A raceme or open panicle with 1 branch per node terminating with a single spikelet; inflorescence to 10 cm long with 5-8 branches and spikelets; pedicels to 3 mm long; spikelets to 19 mm long; 5-12 florets, lower bisexual, upper pistillate; lower glume 1-2.5 mm long, upper to 3.5 mm long; lemmas to 5 mm long, 7-9 veined, apices truncate to rounded, awned or unawned, if awned to 1 mm long; palea keels winged, each with 2 flattened awns.

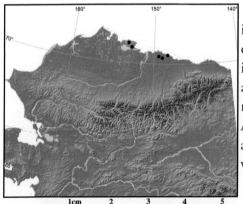

Native riparian grass found in open wet areas and is most often found partially submerged in ponds, lakes, beaded streams, and shorelines of streams and rivers. Restricted to the Arctic in Alaska and is often overlooked as it is generally growing in open water in late summer.

False semaphoregrass

Tribe: Meliceae

growing within *Arctophila fulva*

raceme inflorescence
florets
lemmas
spikelets

awned paleas
paleas

florets

lemma parallel veins

awned paleas

ligule

glumes

29

False melic
Schizachne purpurascens (Torr.) Swallen

Perennial, tufted; open-panicle inflorescence, multiple branches from a single node; membranous ligule, 0.5-1.5 mm long; spikelets relatively small, rounded on the back; glumes papery, shorter than the multiple perfect florets within them, disarticulation of the florets is above the glumes; lemma veins parallel not converging near the tip, awned, often folded together to form a rudiment near the spikelet summit; callus long pilose.

Plants perennial, tufted; culms 3-10 dm tall, hollow, smooth, glabrous; vernation folded; sheaths closed, glabrous, smooth or scaberulous; blades 2-5 mm wide, 5-15 cm long, flat, glabrous, smooth or scaberulous adaxially, smooth abaxially; collars indistinct or yellow, continuous; auricles absent; ligules membranous, 0.5-1.5 mm long, truncate, entire, glabrous.

Panicle about 10 cm long, branches single or in pairs, drooping, each bearing 1 or 2 spikelets; spikelets 11-17 mm long, 3-6 flowered, disarticulating above the glumes; glumes unequal, purplish, first glume 4.2-6.2 mm long, 1-nerved or with 2 other short basal ones, second glume 6-9 mm long, 1-nerved, the laterals short; lemmas lanceolate, 8-10.5 mm long, bidentate, teeth 1-2 mm long, awned from just below teeth, awn 10-15 mm long; paleas about two-thirds as long as lemmas.

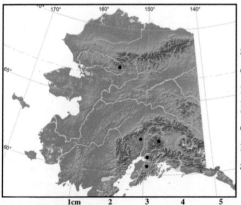

Native grass found scattered in meadows, moist areas of willows, open-canopy forest margins, and moist rocky hillsides. Uncommon grass and often mistaken for a brome or fescue because of its longer lemma awns.

30

False melic

Tribe: Meliceae

open panicle inflorescence

panicle branch

florets

ligule

glumes

inflorescence

Northern mannagrass

Glyceria borealis (Nash) Batch.

Perennial; inflorescence a narrow-appressed panicle, multiple branches from a single node; membranous ligule; spikelets relatively small, rounded on the back; glumes membranous, lower and upper with a single nerve, both shorter than the multiple perfect florets within them, disarticulation of the florets is above the glumes; lemma veins parallel not converging near the tip, glabrous on the keels.

Plants perennial; culms 6-10 dm tall, hollow, smooth, glabrous; often decumbent and rooting at the nodes; vernation folded; sheaths closed, smooth, glabrous, slightly keeled; blades 2-8 mm wide, 8-20 cm long, flat, scurfy adaxially, smooth and glabrous with prominent midrib abaxially; collars yellowish-green, constricted, interrupted; auricles absent; ligules membranous, 5-8.9 mm long, obtuse or acute, lacerate, glabrous.

Panicle narrow, 20-40 cm long, the branches and pedicels appressed; spikelets mostly 6-12 flowered, 10-15 mm long; first glume 2-2.5 mm long, 1-nerved, second glume 3-4 mm long, 1-nerved; lemmas rather thin, obtuse, 3-4 mm long, strongly 7-nerved, scarious at the tip, glabrous between the hispidulous nerves.

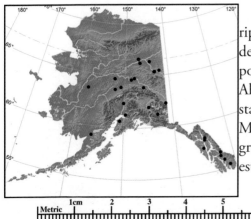

Native cool season riparian grass colonizing deposited sediment of streams, ponds, or lakeshores throughout Alaska. Often growing in standing water in late summer. May decrease as more aggressive grasslike plants become established.

Northern mannagrass
Tribe: Meliceae

spikelets

florets

lemma

dense
papillose
upper
leaf
surface

palea

glumes

upper
glume

ligule

rachilla

florets

lower
glume

Narrow mannagrass
Glyceria leptostachya Buckley

Perennial; inflorescence a narrow-appressed panicle, multiple branches from a single node; membranous ligule; spikelets relatively small, rounded on the back; glumes membranous, lower and upper with a single nerve, both shorter than the multiple perfect florets within them, disarticulation of the florets is above the glumes; lemmas veins parallel not converging near the tip, scabrous on and between the nerves.

Plants perennial; culms 1-15 dm tall, 3-8 mm thick, erect to decumbent and rooting at the lower nodes; sheaths and leaves scabridulous; ligules to12 mm long; blades 12-30 cm long, 3.5-11 mm wide.

Panicle inflorescence to 40 cm long; branches appressed to ascending with up to 8 spikelets; spikelets to 20 mm long with 6-15 florets; glumes rounded to acute, about 1.5-3 mm long; lemmas firm, broadly rounded toward tip, about 3 mm long, 7-nerved, nerves raised and scabridulous.

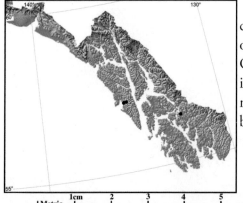

Native riparian grass colonizing deposited sediment of streams, ponds, or lakeshores. Often growing in standing water in late summer. May decrease as more aggressive grasslike plants become established.

Narrow mannagrass

Tribe: Meliceae

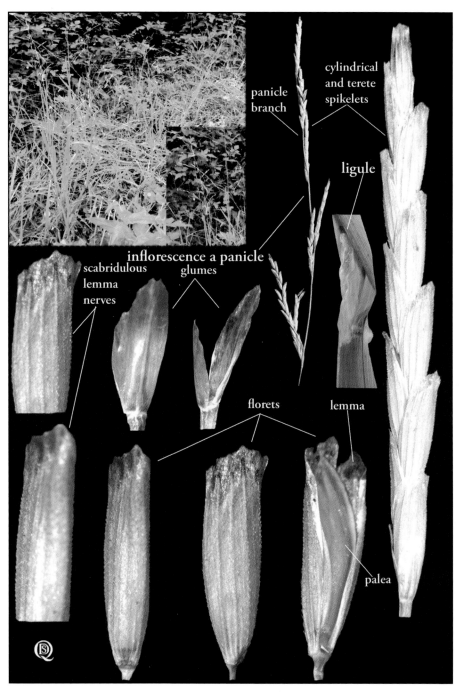

cylindrical and terete spikelets

panicle branch

ligule

inflorescence a panicle

scabridulous lemma nerves

glumes

florets

lemma

palea

Fowl mannagrass; Ridged glyceria
Glyceria striata (Lam.) Hitchc.

Perennial; open-panicle inflorescence; multiple branches from a single node; membranous ligule; leaves 2-6 mm wide; spikelets relatively small, 4 mm long or less; rounded on the back; glumes membranous, lower and upper with a single nerve, both shorter than the multiple perfect florets within them, first or lower glume about 0.5-1.2 mm long; disarticulation of the florets is above the glumes; nerves of the lemma parallel not converging near the tip.

Plants perennial, rhizomatous; culms 2-10 dm tall, hollow, smooth, glabrous; vernation folded; sheaths closed, glabrous, scaberulous, keeled; blades 5-30 cm long, 2-6 mm wide, flat or folded, glabrous, scaberulous or edges scabrous only; collars green or yellow, faint or distinct, continuous or interrupted; auricles absent; ligules membranous, 1.6-3.7 mm long, obtuse or acuminate, closed in front, surrounding culm, tearing easily, entire or erose, glabrous.

Panicle ovoid, open, nodding, 10-20 cm long, the branches solitary and in 3's, ascending at base, drooping, naked below; spikelets 3-7 flowered, ovate to oblong, 1.8-4 mm long; first glume 0.5-1.2 mm long, 1-nerved, second glume 0.6-1.2 mm long, 1-nerved; lemmas 1.2-2 mm long, prominently 7-nerved, obtuse to oblong; palea rather firm, about as long as the lemma, the smooth keels prominent, bowed.

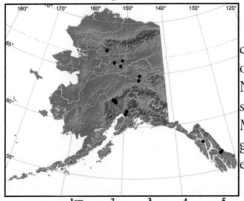

Native riparian grass colonizing deposited sediment of streams, ponds, or lake shores. Not often found growing in standing water in late summer. May decrease as more aggressive grasslike plants become established.

36

Fowl mannagrass; Ridged glyceria

Tribe: Meliceae

glumes

parallel veins

florets

drooping panicle inflorescence

glumes 1-nerved

florets

lemma

palea

rachilla

lemma

lower glume

spikelets

upper glume

ligule

panicle branch

Tall glyceria, English watergrass
Glyceria maxima (Hartm.) Holmb.

Perennial; plants stout and tall; open-panicle inflorescence; multiple branches from a single node; membranous ligule; leaves 6-20 mm wide; spikelets relatively small, 5-12 mm long; somewhat laterally compressed; glumes membranous, lower and upper with a single nerve, both shorter than the multiple perfect florets within them, first or lower glume usually longer than 2 mm, upper 3-4 mm long; disarticulation of the florets is above the glumes; nerves of the lemma parallel not converging near the tip.

Plants perennial; rhizomatous culms to 25 dm tall, to 12 mm thick; sheaths scabridulous; ligules to 6 mm long; blades to 6 dm long, 6-20 mm wide.

Open-panicle inflorescence, to 4.5 dm long, 3 dm wide, branches to 2 dm long, drooping at maturity with over 50 spikelets; spikelets to 12 mm long, 2-3 mm wide with up to 10 florets, somewhat laterally compressed; glumes 3-4 mm long, longer than wide, lower 2-3 mm long, upper 3-4 mm long; lemmas 3-4 mm long; 7-veined, veins scabridulous.

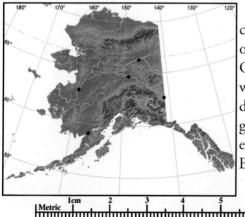

Introduced riparian grass colonizing deposited sediment of streams, ponds or lakeshores. Often found growing in standing water in late summer. May decrease as more aggressive grasslike plants become established. Used for fodder in Europe.

Tall glyceria, English watergrass
Tribe: Meliceae

leaf blades 6-20 mm wide

panicle branch

upper glume 3-4 mm long

culms 6-12 mm thick

spikelets

florets

anthers

palea

lemma

stigma

spikelets somewhat laterally compressed

American mannagrass
Glyceria grandis S. Watson

Perennial; plants stout and tall; open-panicle inflorescence; multiple branches from a single node; membranous ligule; leaves 6-12 mm wide; spikelets relatively small, 5-6 mm long; somewhat laterally compressed; glumes membranous, lower and upper with a single nerve, both shorter than the multiple perfect florets within them, first or lower glume usually longer than 2 mm, upper to 2.7 mm long; disarticulation of the florets is above the glumes; nerves of the lemma parallel not converging near the tip.

Plants perennial, rhizomatous; culms 10-15 dm tall, hollow, smooth, glabrous; vernation folded; sheaths closed, smooth, glabrous, keeled, inflated; blades 6-12 mm wide, 15-40 cm long, flat, glabrous, scaberulous adaxially and on edges, smooth abaxially; collars yellow, constricted, continuous; auricles absent; ligules membranous, 2.7-3.7 mm long, closed in front, surrounding culm, tearing easily, entire, glabrous.

Panicle large, open at maturity, nodding at summit, 20-40 cm long; branches to 1.8 dm long; spikelets 3.2-10 mm long, 4-7 florets, first glume 1-2.3 mm long, 1-nerved, second glume 1.5-2.7 mm long, 1-nerved; lemmas about 2.5 mm long, 7-nerved; palea rather thin, about as long as the lemma.

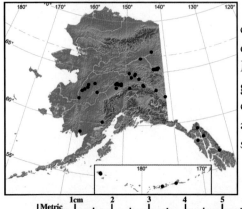

Native riparian grass colonizing deposited sediment of streams, ponds, or lakeshores. May decrease as more aggressive grasslike plants become established. May have value as a commercially produced seed source for wetland reclamation.

American mannagrass
Tribe: Meliceae

large open panicle inflorescence

spikelets

panicle branch

lemma

florets

palea

single nerved glumes

glumes

glabrous ligule

spikelets

Beautiful glyceria, Mackenzie Valley mannagrass
Glyceria pulchella (Nash) K. Schum.

Perennial; plants slender, culms to 6 dm tall; open-panicle inflorescence; multiple branches from a single node; membranous ligule; leaves to about 29 cm long, 2-7.5 mm wide; spikelets relatively small, to 6 mm long, somewhat laterally compressed; glumes membranous, lower and upper with a single nerve, both shorter than the multiple perfect florets within them, first or lower glume about 2 mm, upper to 2.6 mm long; disarticulation of the florets is above the glumes; nerves of the lemma parallel, not converging near the tip, with an erose apex.

Plants perennial; culms to 6 dm tall, 1.5-5 mm thick; ligules 1.5-4 mm long; blades to about 29 cm long, to 2-7.5 mm wide, scabrous.

Open-panicle inflorescence, 15-25 cm long, to 20 cm wide, nodding at maturity; branches to 12 cm long, ascending to divergent, flexuous with up to or over 40 spikelets; spikelets to 6 mm long, to about 3 mm wide, somewhat laterally compressed, 3-6 florets; lower glumes 1.5-2 mm long, upper 2-2.6 mm long; lemmas 2.5-3.5 mm long, 7-veined and veins raised, scabridulous apices broadly acute to obtuse and often erose.

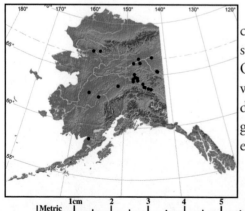

Native riparian grass colonizing deposited sediment of streams, ponds or lakeshores. Often found growing in standing water in late summer. May decrease as more aggressive grasslike plants become established.

Beautiful glyceria, Mackenzie Valley mannagrass

Tribe: Meliceae

branch with few spikelets

open panicle inflorescence

7-nerved lemmas

spikelet

branch and spikelets

raised nerves of the lemmas

palea

glumes

lemma broad scarious margins and erose at top

rachilla

stigma

Alaska melic

Melica subulata (Griseb.) Scribn.

Perennial, tufted or with short rhizomes; appressed-panicle inflorescence, multiple short branches from a single node; membranous ligule; spikelets relatively small, rounded on the back; glumes papery, shorter than the multiple perfect florets within them, disarticulation of the florets is above the glumes; callus glabrous; lemmas firm, apices strongly tapering and acuminate, unawned.

Plants perennial, tufted or short rhizomes; culms 6-12.5 dm tall, hollow, smooth, glabrous, swollen bases attached to rhizome by slender stems; vernation rolled; sheaths closed, glabrous, scaberulous, keeled; blades 2-10 mm wide, flat, glabrous, scaberulous; collars yellow, continuous, chevron shaped; auricles absent; ligules membranous, 1.5-2 mm long, acute, erose, glabrous.

Panicle 10-20 cm long, usually narrow; spikelets narrow, 10-20 mm long, loosely 2- to 5-flowered; glumes acute, narrow, obscurely nerved, first glume averaging 5 mm long, second glume about 8 mm long, purple or brown-tinged; callus glabrous; lemmas 9-12 mm long, narrow, tapering to an acuminate point, awnless, prominently 7-nerved, frequently pilose, ciliate on the backs; rudiment 5-8 mm long; anthers 2 mm long.

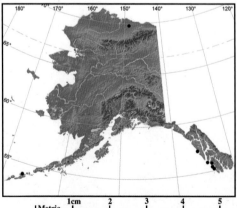

Uncommon native grass found in moist woods, along streambanks, and on shady slopes of coastal Alaska.

Alaska melic

Tribe: Meliceae

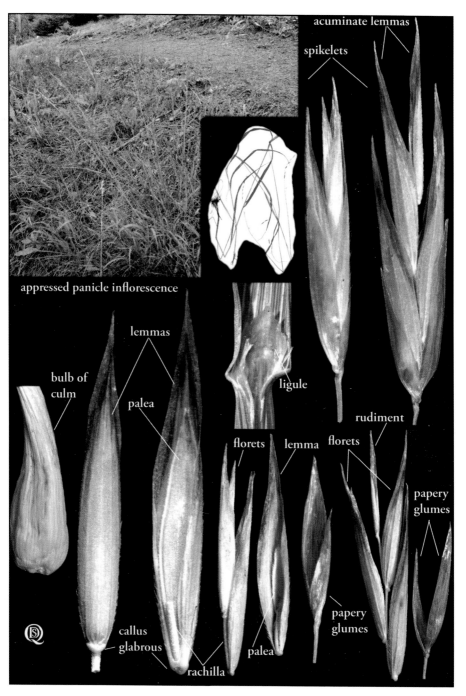

acuminate lemmas

spikelets

appressed panicle inflorescence

lemmas

bulb of culm

palea

ligule

florets

lemma

florets

rudiment

papery glumes

callus glabrous

rachilla

palea

papery glumes

45

Cheatgrass brome, Downy brome

Bromus tectorum L.

Anisantha tectorum (L.) Nevski

Annual; inflorescence an open spreading and often drooping panicle; ligule membranous; spikelets relatively large 12-20 mm long, multiple fertile florets; both glumes present, lower 1 veined, upper 3-5 veined; lemma veins converging near the apex, exceeding the glumes, 9-12 mm long, narrow, bifid; straight awns 10-18 mm long.

Plants annual; culms up to 6 dm tall, hollow, smooth, glabrous or pubescent, erect or decumbent; vernation rolled; sheaths closed, smooth, glabrous or pubescent, sometimes pilose on margins; blades 3-7 mm wide, flat or involute, smooth, pubescent; collars glabrous or pilose, yellow, continuous; auricles absent; ligules membranous, 2-3 mm long, acute, lacerate, glabrous.

Panicle 5-15 cm long, rather dense, soft, drooping, broad, often purple; spikelets 12-20 mm long, 5-8 flowered, nodding, glabrous or hairy; first glume 4-6 mm long, 1-nerved, second glume 8-10 mm long, 3-5 nerved; lemmas 9-12 mm long, the apical teeth to 3 mm long, lanceolate, awns 10-18 mm long.

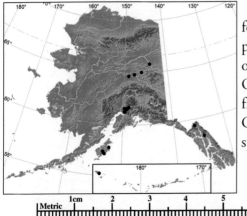

Introduced annual grass found in disturbed areas. Likely present in farmed areas, roadsides, or ports where ships are unloaded. Occupies a wide range of habitats from uplands to riparian zones. Generally considered a weedy species.

Cheatgrass brome, Downy brome

Tribe: Bromeae

ligule

straight long awns

lemma

floret

palea

glumes

spikelet

floret

glumes

Soft chess

Bromus hordeaceus L.
Bromus mollis L.

Annual; inflorescence an erect-contracted panicle 1-13 cm long, pedicels shorter than the spikelets; ligule membranous; spikelets relatively large; both glumes present, lower 3-5 nerves, upper 5-7 nerves, broad, obtuse; multiple fertile florets; lemmas short, veins converging near the apex, bifid, exceeding the glumes; awn rather stout, 6-8 mm long.

Plants annual; lower sheaths softly pubescent throughout; culms erect, 20-80 cm tall; ligules to 1.5 mm long; blades to 19 cm long, to 4 mm wide.

Panicle erect, contracted, 1-13 cm long, shorter in depauperate plants, reduced to a few spikelets; spikelet glumes broad, obtuse, coarsely pilose or scabrous pubescent, the first 5-7 mm long, 3-5 nerves, the second 6.5-8 mm long, 5-7 nerves; lemmas 6.5-11 mm long, broad, soft, obtuse, 7-9 nerved, coarsely pilose or scabrous pubescent, rather deeply bidentate, the margin and apex hyaline; awn rather stout, 6-8 mm long; palea about three-fourths as long as the lemma.

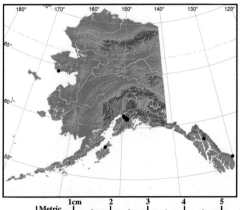

Introduced grass usually found in disturbed areas. Most likely found along transportation corridors and commercial developments.

Soft chess

Tribe: Bromeae

spikelets

short
panicle
branches

ligule

spikelet

floret

glumes

upper glume

lower glume

palea

lemma

glumes

pubescent
sheath and
leaf blades

49

Chess brome

Bromus secalinus L.

Annual; open, nodding, or drooping panicle inflorescence, some pedicels longer than the spikelets; ligule membranous; spikelets relatively large; both glumes present, multiple fertile florets; sheaths and lemmas glabrous; lemmas exceeding the glumes; lower glume 4-6 mm long, 3-5 veined, upper glume 6-7 mm long, 7 veined; the margins of the lemma inrolled toward the base at maturity, broad, abruptly narrowed above, not inflated, the awn mostly shorter than the body.

Plants annual; culms 3-6 dm tall, hollow, smooth, glabrous; vernation rolled; sheaths closed, smooth, glabrous or puberulent; blades flat, smooth and pilose adaxially, scabrous and glabrous abaxially; collars yellow or brownish, interrupted; auricles absent; ligules membranous, 1.1-1.6 mm long, obtuse, erose, glabrous.

Panicle pyramidal, drooping, 8-15 cm long, open, the lower branches 3-5 at a node, unequal, longer than the spikelet; spikelets 10-20 mm long, 6-8 mm wide, ovoid-lanceolate, becoming somewhat turgid at maturity; first glume 4-6 mm long, 3- to 5-nerved, second glume 6-7 mm long, 7-nerved, both glumes obtuse; lemmas 6-8 mm long, 7-nerved, elliptic, obtuse, smooth or scabrous, the margins strongly involute in fruit, apex shortly bidentate, the undulate awn 3-5 mm long, sometimes short or obsolete; palea about as long as the lemma.

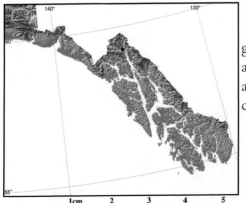

Reportedly introduced grass usually found in disturbed areas. When present, likely found along transportation corridors and commercial developments.

Chess brome

Tribe: Bromeae

ligule

lemmas beginning
to fold around
the palea and then
caryopsis

palea
as long or
longer than
lemma

palea

panicle inflorescence

spikelets
with short to
very short and
fragile awns

florets

rachilla
internode

glumes

rachilla
internodes
visible at
maturity

Sitka brome; Alaska brome

Bromus sitchensis Trin.

Perennial, loosely tufted; inflorescence an open panicle; lower branches to 20 cm long; ligule membranous; spikelets relatively large, flattened, both glumes present, multiple fertile florets; lemmas strongly compressed, bifid apex, awned, exceeding the glumes.

Plants perennial; loosely tufted; culms to 18 dm tall and 5 mm thick; sheaths mostly glabrous; ligules to 4 mm long; blades to 40 cm long and 9 mm wide, flat.

Inflorescence an open panicle; lower branches 10-20 cm long, to 6 per node, spreading and often drooping; 1-3 spikelets per branch on the distal half or confined to the end; spikelets to 3.8 cm long, strongly flattened, 6-9 florets; glumes to 9 veined and 11 mm long; lemmas to 15 mm long, strongly laterally compressed, strongly keeled distally, often with acute teeth shorter than 1 mm long; awns to 10 mm long; anthers to 6 mm long.

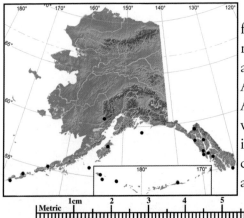

Native grass growing in forest borders, open areas, roadsides, and disturbed areas along the coast of the Aleutian Islands and southeastern Alaska. A tall and robust grass with a large and open panicle inflorescence. Has potential commercial value in revegetation and land reclamation.

Sitka brome; Alaska brome

Tribe: Bromeae

ligule

panicle branches long
and often drooping

palea

lemma

floret

glumes

compressed
spikelets

Aleutian brome

Bromus aleutensis Trin. *ex* Griseb.

Bromus sitchensis var. *aleutensis* Trin. *ex* (Griseb.) Hultén

Perennial, loosely tufted; inflorescence an open panicle; lower branches less than 10 cm long; culms greater than 3 mm thick; ligule membranous; spikelets relatively large, flattened, both glumes present, multiple fertile florets; lemmas strongly compressed, bifid apex, awned, exceeding the glumes.

Plants perennial; loosely tufted; culms to 13 dm tall and 7 mm thick; sheaths striate, pilose to moderately dense; ligules to 5 mm long; blades to 35 cm long and 15 mm wide, flat.

Inflorescence an open panicle; lower branches to 10 cm long, 1-2 per node, stiffly ascending; 1-3 spikelets per branch on the distal half or confined to the end; spikelets to 4 cm long, strongly flattened, 3-6 florets; glumes to 9 veined and 15 mm long; lemmas to 17 mm long strongly laterally compressed, strongly keeled distally, often with acute teeth shorter than 1 mm long; awns to 10 mm long; anthers to 4.2 mm long.

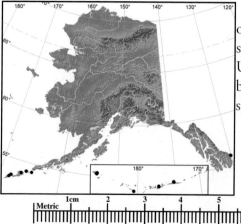

Native grass found mostly on disturbed soils of roads, lake shores, and disturbed streambanks. Uncommon and easily recognized by its robust size and large spikelets.

Aleutian brome

Tribe: Bromeae

open panicle inflorescence

lemmas

palea

panicle branches stiff and short

florets

glumes

ligule

florets

rachilla

spikelet

Mountain brome

Bromus carinatus var. *marginatus* Barkworth & Anderton
Bromus marginatus Nees *ex* Steud.

Perennial, tufted; inflorescence an appressed to open panicle; lower branches less than 10 cm long; culms less than 3 mm thick; ligule membranous; spikelets relatively large, flattened, both glumes present, multiple fertile florets; lemmas strongly compressed, exceeding the glumes, keeled, bifid apex, awned, awns 3-10 mm long.

Plants perennial, tufted; culms 2.5-10 dm tall, less than 3 mm thick, hollow, smooth, nodes puberulent to pubescent or shortly pilose; vernation rolled; sheaths closed, smooth, glabrous, canescent, pilose or margins pilose only; blades 1-12 mm wide, flat, glabrous, pilose or canescent, scabrous or scabrous adaxially and smooth abaxially; collars glabrous or pilose, yellow, continuous; auricles absent; ligules membranous, 1.4-2.7 mm long, obtuse or acute, entire, erose or lacerate, glabrous.

Panicle 5-40 cm long, erect; branches spreading, ascending or appressed, lower to 10 cm long; spikelets 20-40 mm long, 5-11 flowered; glumes lanceolate, smooth or scaberulous, the first glume 6-11 mm long, 3-7 nerved, the second 9-12 mm long, 3-9 nerved; lemmas 11-14 mm long, 7-9 nerved, glabrous to pubescent, the awns 3-10 mm long from between bifid apices.

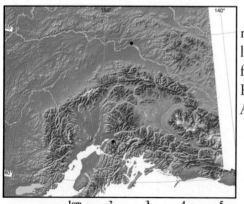

Introduced grass that may be found in disturbed areas like roadsides and right-of-ways for utility lines. Common in the Rocky Mountains but rare in Alaska.

open to
appressed
panicle

lemma

lemma   glumes

palea

compressed spikelets

palea

ligule

Smooth brome

Bromus inermis Leyss.

Perennial, rhizomatous; inflorescence an open panicle; spikelets little flattened, rounded on the back, many flowered and relatively large; glumes 2 and usually shorter than the lowest floret; ligule membranous; lemmas seldom or only slightly bifid, rounded on the back, awnless or no longer than about 3 mm.

Plants perennial, rhizomatous; culms 4.6-10.7 dm tall, hollow, smooth, nodes pubescent to pilose; vernation rolled; sheaths closed, smooth, glabrous, puberulent or pilose; blades 5-12 mm wide, flat, glabrous, puberulent or pilose, smooth or scaberulous, edges scabrous; collars yellow to green, continuous or interrupted, sometimes constricted; auricles absent, or present, 1.2 mm long; ligules membranous, 0.4-2 mm long, truncate or obtuse, erose or ciliolate, glabrous.

Panicle 10-20 cm long, narrow, erect, the branches spreading at anthesis, contracted at maturity, green, reddish or purplish; spikelets 20-30 mm long, 5-11 flowered; glumes glabrous or pubescent, the first glume 4-8 mm long, 1-nerved, the second 6-9 mm long, 3-nerved; lemmas 9-12 mm long, 5-7 nerved, glabrous or pubescent, obtuse, emarginate, mucronate or with awns 1-3 mm long.

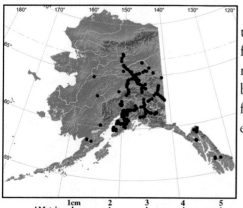

Introduced grass common to disturbed areas like roadsides, floodplains, streambanks, irrigated meadows, and right-of-ways. Has been extensively planted in Alaska for both forage and revegetation/erosion control of disturbed areas.

Smooth brome
Tribe: Bromeae

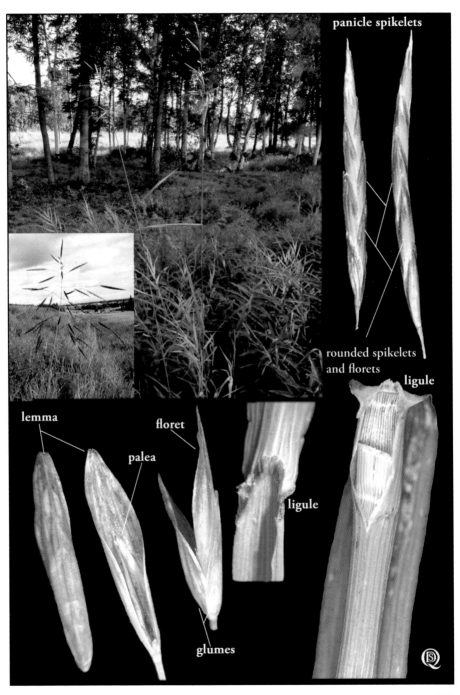

panicle spikelets

rounded spikelets and florets

ligule

lemma

floret

palea

ligule

glumes

Arctic brome
Bromus pumpellianus Scribn. subsp. *pumpellianus*

Perennial, very rhizomatous with few culms together; inflorescence an open panicle; spikelets little flattened, rounded on the back, many flowered and relatively large; glumes 2 and usually shorter than the lowest floret; ligule membranous; lemmas seldom or only slightly bifid, rounded on the back, lemmas awned, to 7.5 mm long.

Plants perennial, very rhizomatous; culms 5-12 dm tall, erect, nodes 2-3, usually pubescent, sometimes glabrous; internodes glabrous or pubescent; sheaths pilose, villous, or glabrous; auricles present on the lower leaves or absent; ligules 1.5-3 mm long; blades 9-17 cm long, 4-8 mm wide, abaxial surfaces glabrous or pilose, adaxial surfaces usually pilose, rarely glabrous.

Panicles 10-20 cm long, open or contracted, erect or nodding; branches erect to spreading; spikelets 20-30 mm long; glumes glabrous, pubescent, or hirsute; lower glumes 5-9 mm long, 1-veined; upper glumes 8-11 mm long, 3-veined; lemmas 9-14 mm long, pubescent on the lower portion of the back and along the margins; awns usually present, to 7.5 mm long, sometimes absent.

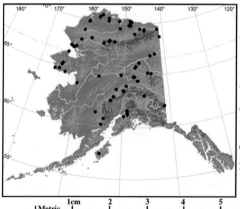

Native grass found growing on rock outcrops, rocky hillsides, dry areas of pingos, and hummocks. Not abundant but widely scattered throughout open dry tundra and meadow habitat. Used in a cross with *B. inermis* to develop 'Polar' brome, a cultivar forage grass used in Alaska.

60

Arctic brome

Tribe: Bromeae

palea

lemma

pubescent
spikelet

branches and spikelets

glabrous to
hairy
spikelet

florets

florets

glumes

palea

florets

glumes

ligule

lemma

ligule

61

Arctic brome

Bromus pumpellianus subsp. *dicksonii* W.W. Mitch. & Wilton

Perennial, tufted in appearance; shortly rhizomatous; many culms together; inflorescence an open panicle; spikelets little flattened, rounded on the back, many flowered and relatively large; glumes 2 and usually shorter than the lowest floret; ligule membranous; lemmas seldom or only slightly bifid, rounded on the back, lemmas awned, up to 7.5 mm long.

Plants perennial, tufted; rhizomes short when present; culms to 13.5 dm tall, ascending, often geniculate; 3-7 nodes; internodes glabrous; auricles may be present; ligules membranous, up to 4 mm long; blades up to 30 cm long and up to 9 mm wide, flat.

Open panicle inflorescence, to 24 cm long, nodding to erect; spikelets to 45 mm long; lower glume up to 10 mm long, upper up to 13 mm long, 3-veined; lemmas up to 16 mm long, exceeding the glumes; awns up to 7.5 mm long; anthers to 6 mm long.

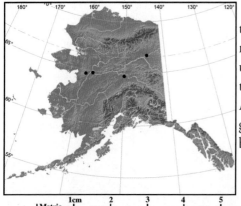

Native grass restricted to the Yukon River corridor and major tributaries. Other than its unique location, this grass may be the introduced forage grass, *B. riparius*. When present, it grows on rocky bluffs and river banks.

Arctic brome

Tribe: Bromeae

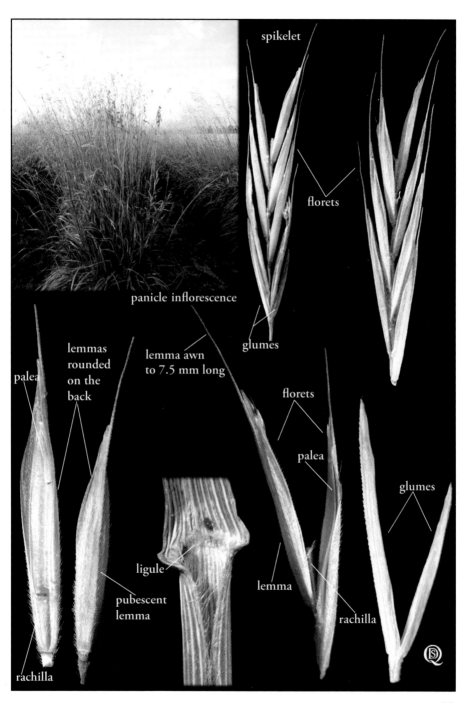

spikelet

florets

panicle inflorescence

glumes

lemmas rounded on the back

palea

lemma awn to 7.5 mm long

florets

palea

glumes

ligule

pubescent lemma

lemma

rachilla

rachilla

Pacific brome
Bromus pacificus Shear

Perennial, tufted, rhizomes lacking; inflorescence a large open panicle; spikelets little flattened, rounded on the back, many flowered and relatively large; glumes 2 and usually shorter than the lowest floret, pubescent, rarely glabrous; ligule membranous; lemmas slightly bifid, rounded on the back, awned; awns to 7 mm long; anthers 2-4 mm long.

Plants perennial, tufted; rhizomes lacking; culms to 17 dm tall, erect, to 8 nodes; auricles absent; ligules membranous, to 1 mm long; leaf blades to 24 cm long, to 14 mm wide, flat.

Panicle 10-25 cm, open, branches ascending to spreading or drooping; spikelets to 30 mm long, terete to somewhat laterally compressed, to 10 florets; glumes pubescent, lower 1-3 nerved, up to 8 mm long, upper 3-nerved, to 12 mm long; lemmas rounded on the back, to 15 mm long, pubescent to glabrous on the margins and backs; awns up to 7 mm long; anthers 2-4 mm long.

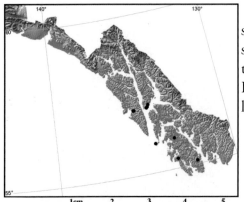

Native grass growing in shaded moist woods, ravines, and slopes. In Alaska, it is restricted to the Southeast maritime region. Recognized by its tall size and large rounded spikelets with awns.

Pacific brome
Tribe: Bromeae

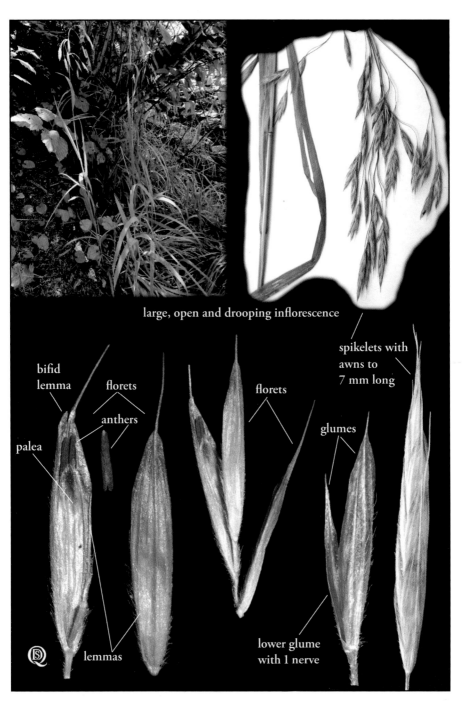

large, open and drooping inflorescence

bifid lemma

florets

anthers

palea

florets

spikelets with awns to 7 mm long

glumes

lemmas

lower glume with 1 nerve

Fringed brome
Bromus ciliatus L.

Perennial, tufted, rhizomes lacking; inflorescence an open panicle, often nodding; ligule membranous, less than 1 mm long; spikelets little flattened, rounded on the back, many flowered; glumes 2 and usually shorter than the lowest floret, usually glabrous; lemmas often bifid, rounded on the back, pubescent only on the margins near the base or glabrous over the entire back; awns to 5 mm long; anthers 1-1.4 mm long.

Plants perennial, tufted; culms 5-15 dm tall, hollow, smooth, glabrous or nodes pilose; vernation rolled; sheaths closed, smooth, pilose; blades 5-10 mm wide, flat, glabrous, smooth to scaberulous; collars yellowish, purplish or indistinct, glabrous or pilose at front; auricles absent; ligules membranous, 0.4-1 mm long, truncate, erose, glabrous.

Panicle 15-25 cm long, broad, the branches slender, drooping, as much as 15 cm long; spikelets 15-20 mm long, 5-to 11-flowered; first glume 6-8 mm long, 1 nerved, second glume 8-11 mm long, 3-nerved; lemmas 10-14 mm long, 3-to-5-nerved, oblong-lanceolate, pubescent near the margin on the lower one-half to three-fourths, glabrous or nearly so on the back, awns 3-5 mm long, slender, straight; anthers 1-1.4 mm long.

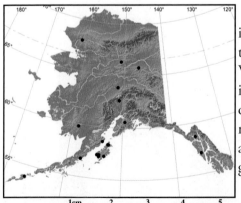

Native grass usually found in moist meadows, willow thickets, and on streambanks. While widespread through Alaska, it is never present in large quantities. Recognized, when mature by its nodding panicle and average spikelet length for a brome grass.

Fringed brome

Tribe: Bromeae

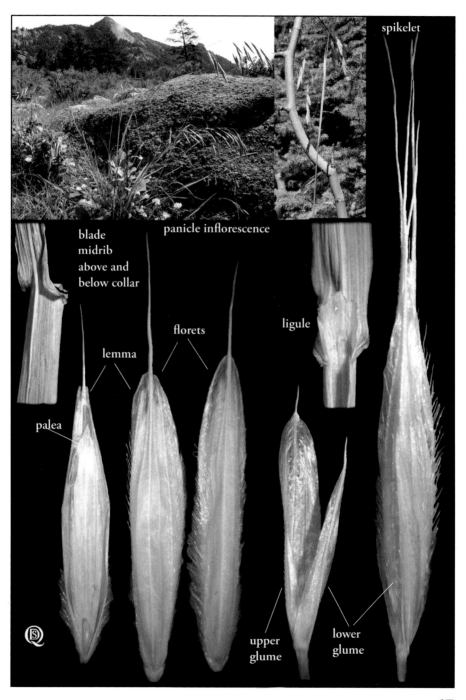

spikelet

blade
midrib
above and
below collar

panicle inflorescence

florets

ligule

lemma

palea

upper
glume

lower
glume

Richardson's brome

Bromus richardsonii Link

Perennial, tufted, rhizomes lacking; inflorescence an open panicle, often nodding; ligule membranous, less than 1 mm long; spikelets little flattened, rounded on the back, many flowered; glumes 2 and usually shorter than the lowest floret, usually glabrous; lemmas often bifid, rounded on the back, upper lemmas pubescent and the lower glabrous across the backs; awns to 5 mm long; anthers up to 2.7 mm long.

Plants perennial, rhizomes lacking; culms up to 15 dm tall; nodes usually glabrous; auricles absent; ligules up to 2 mm long; leaf blades to 35 cm long and 12 mm wide, flat.

Panicles up to 25 cm long, open and nodding when mature; spikelets usually up to 20 mm long, terete to moderately laterally compressed, up to 15 florets; glumes usually glabrous, lower to 12 mm long, upper to 16 mm long; lemmas to 16 mm long, rounded on the back, margins densely pilose along the lower ¾, lower lemmas glabrous across the backs, uppermost with appressed hairs on the backs; awns up to 5 mm long, straight; anthers up to 2.7 mm long.

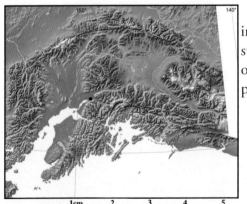

Native grass usually found in moist open woods and shaded streambanks. Rather rare and often confused with the more prevalent *B. ciliatus*.

Richardson's brome
Tribe: Bromeae

blade midrib
at and below
collar

ligule

panicle inflorescence

lemma
margins
conspicuously
hirsute
or densely
pilose

lemma

upper
glume
3 nerved

glabrous
glumes

spikelets

palea

rachilla

lower
glume
single
nerve

glumes

Reed polargrass

Arctagrostis latifolia subsp. *arundinacea* (Trin.) Tzvelev

Perennial, rhizomatous, tall; inflorescence an open and large panicle, branches 3-27 cm long; membranous ligule; spikelet with a single and perfect floret, nerves converging near the apex; glumes 1 mm or longer; lemma exceeding at least 1 glume.

Plants perennial and rhizomatous, rhizomes short to elongate; culms to 15 dm tall, to 7 mm thick; ligules membranous, usually to 7 mm long; leaf blades to 36 cm long and to 15 mm wide; uppermost sheaths shorter than the blades.

Panicles 10-44 cm long; longest branches 3-27 cm long, 50-140 spikelets per branch; all branches usually spreading; spikelets 3-5.2 mm long; glumes unequal, upper varying from shorter to longer than the lemma.

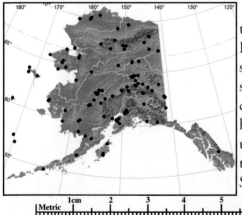

Native grass of meadows, taller willows, and forest margins. Recognized by several long and spreading branches leaving the same spot on a single side of the culm. Two commercial cultivars have been developed in Alaska and used for revegetation projects in the Arctic, Interior, and Southcentral regions.

Reed polargrass
Tribe: Poeae

open panicle inflorescence

panicle branch

spikelets

upper glume longer than lemma

palea

florets

lemma

lower glume shorter than lemma

unawned glumes

ligule

71

Polargrass
Arctagrostis latifolia (R.Br.) Griseb. subsp. *latifolia*

Perennial, rhizomatous; inflorescence usually a contracted panicle, longest branches usually to 4 cm long; membranous ligule; spikelet with a single perfect floret, nerves converging near the apex; glumes 1 mm or longer; lemma exceeding at least 1 glume.

Plants perennial and rhizomatous, rhizomes short to elongate; culms to 9.5 dm tall, to 7 mm thick; ligules membranous, usually to 7 mm long; leaf blades to 16 cm long and to 9 mm wide; uppermost sheaths longer than the blades.

Panicles 2.5-17 cm long; longest branches usually to 4 cm long, 3-40 spikelets per branch; secondary branches usually appressed; spikelets 3-6.5 mm long; glumes subequal to somewhat unequal, both just shorter than the lemma.

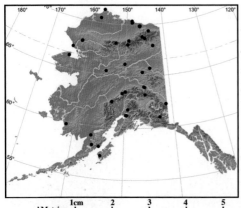

Native grass common to the short willow and tundra of the Arctic and high elevation alpine habitat. A prevalent grass easily recognized by several short branches leaving the same spot on a single side of the culm. Often mistaken for the appressed panicle *Calamagrostis* species.

Polargrass

Tribe: Poeae

appressed panicle inflorescence

panicle branch

stigma

spikelets

ligule

florets

stamens

palea

stigma

lemma

anthers

lemma

lower glume shorter than lemma

upper glume longer than lemma

upper glume

lower glume

stigma

Common icegrass
Phippsia algida (Sol.) R. Br.

Perennial, tufted; less than 1 dm tall; inflorescence usually a contracted panicle; membranous ligule; spikelet with a single perfect floret, nerves converging near the apex; glumes less than 1 mm long, the lower minute; lemma exceeding at least 1 glume.

Plants perennial, tufted; culms less than 1 dm tall, hollow, smooth, glabrous; vernation folded; sheaths closed, smooth, glabrous; blades less than 10 cm long, folded, boat tipped, smooth, glabrous; collars indistinct, or yellow, continuous; auricles absent; ligules membranous, 1 mm long, truncate or obtuse, entire, glabrous.

Panicle oblong to linear-oblong, loose, 2-3 cm long, few spikelets, spikelets 1-flowered, disarticulating above the glumes; glumes unequal, upper subequal to as long as the lemma, to 0.6 mm long, lower minute, to 0.3 mm long; lemma to 1.8 mm long, broad, obscurely 3-nerved, keeled, abruptly acute, the apex minutely denticulate; palea 2-keeled, 2-4 toothed at the apex, shorter than the lemma.

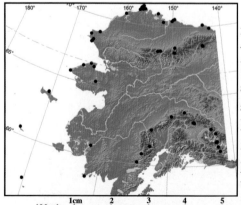

Native riparian grass found on bare disturbed areas of wet sand and gravel deposits below persistent snowbanks in alpine, wet tundra of the Arctic and Chukchi Sea coasts and lakeshores. A colonizer and replaced by other more aggressive plants as disturbed areas matures to wet tundra and meadows.

Common icegrass

Tribe: Poeae

alpine tundra

ocean beach

beach

mountains

beach

anthers

palea

lemma

spikelets

panicle branches

floret

anthers

floret

caryopsis

lemma

palea

ligule

glumes

Common timothy

Phleum pratense L.

Perennial, tufted; culms erect, from a swollen bulb-like base, to 15 dm tall; membranous ligule; inflorescence a dense-spicate and cylindric panicle, much longer than wide; spikelets strongly keeled, mostly disarticulating above the glumes; glumes short awned containing a single fertile floret; lemmas included within the glumes, awnless.

Plants perennial, tufted; culms 5-15 dm tall, hollow, smooth, glabrous, bases swollen; vernation rolled; sheaths open, smooth, glabrous; blades 4-8 mm wide, 7-20 cm long, flat or loosely involute, glabrous, smooth adaxially, scabrous above abaxially, edges scabrous; collars indistinct, or yellow, interrupted; auricles absent; ligules membranous, 2.2-2.6 mm long, obtuse or shortly acuminate, ciliolate, glabrous.

Panicle dense, cylindric, spikelike, 5-15 cm long or more, 5-8 mm wide; spikelets strongly flattened, 3-4 mm long, 1-flowered; glumes equal, body about 3.5 mm long, 3-nerved, membranous, ciliate on the keels, abruptly truncate at apex with a stout awn about 1-1.7 mm long; lemma about two-thirds as long as the glumes, membranous, hyaline, truncate, 5-7 nerved; palea narrow, nearly as long as the lemma.

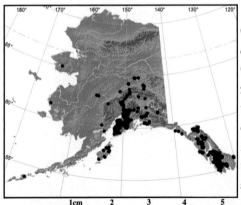

Introduced riparian grass. Cultivated for forage, but has escaped to many habitats. Occupies moist to dry riparian zones at lower elevations Used to reseed disturbed areas, but may dominate and eliminate existing native species. Efforts are now underway to replace this species in all revegetation efforts.

Common timothy
Tribe: Poeae

awned glumes

stigma

dense spicate
panicle
inflorescence

spikelets

glume

anther

ligule

floret

Alpine timothy
Phleum alpinum L.

Perennial, tufted; culms from a decumbent somewhat creeping slender base, 2-5 dm tall; membranous ligule; inflorescence a dense-spicate and cylindric panicle, usually not 4 times as long as wide; spikelets strongly keeled, mostly disarticulating above the glumes; glumes conspicuously short awned, containing a single fertile floret; lemmas included within the glumes, awnless.

Plants perennial, tufted; culms 2-5 dm tall, erect or decumbent, hollow, smooth, glabrous; vernation rolled; sheaths open, smooth, glabrous, inflated; blades 4-6 mm wide, up to 10 cm long, flat, glabrous, sides smooth, edges scabrous; collars yellow, continuous, frequently oblique; auricles absent; ligules membranous, 2.2-3.3 mm long, truncate or obtuse, erose, glabrous.

Panicle 1-5 cm long, 8-12 mm wide when pressed, ellipsoid or short-cylindric, bristly; glumes about 5 mm long, hispid-ciliate on the keel, the awns 1.4-2.6 mm long; lemmas 1.7-2.5 mm long, erose-toothed, awnless.

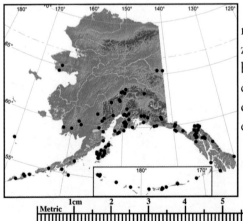

Native grass occupying moist to drier areas of riparian zones. Common and will likely be developed into a commercial cultivar for use in stabilizing disturbed areas of higher elevations and as a possible forage.

Alpine timothy
Tribe: Poeae

dense spicate panicle

florets

awned glumes

anthers

spikelets

palea

lemma

ligule

79

Meadow foxtail

Alopecurus pratensis L.

Perennial, tufted; membranous ligule; inflorescence a dense-spicate and cylindric panicle; spikelets strongly keeled, disarticulating below the glumes, 4-6 mm long; glumes awnless containing a single fertile floret; lemmas included within the glumes, short awned.

Plants perennial, tufted; culms 3-5 dm tall, hollow, smooth, glabrous, green or glaucous, erect, decumbent or geniculate; vernation rolled; sheaths open, smooth, glabrous, green or glaucous, inflated; blades 2-6 mm wide, flat, glabrous, sides smooth, edges scabrous; collars yellow, constricted, interrupted; auricles absent; ligules membranous, 2.8-3.3 mm long, truncate or obtuse, entire or erose-ciliolate, glabrous.

Panicle 3-7 cm long, 7-10 mm wide; glumes about 5 mm long, villous on the keel and pubescent on the sides, awnless; lemma 3-5 mm long, awn exserted 2-5 mm beyond the glumes.

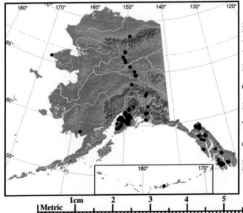

Introduced riparian grass in very wet irrigated meadow soils. No longer recommended for reclamation or pastures, since it decreases the presence of other native grasses. May be confused with *A. arundinaceus*, 'Garrison' creeping foxtail, which was widely planted during the 1970's and 1980's.

Meadow foxtail

Tribe: Poeae

dense spicate panicle

floret awns

florets

spikelets

glumes not awned

glumes

hairy glumes

ligule

Alpine foxtail

Alopecurus magellanicus Lam.

Alopecurus borealis Trin.; *A. alpinus* Vill.

Perennial, tufted; membranous ligule; inflorescence an oblong or ovoid dense-spicate and cylindric panicle, about 1 cm wide; spikelets strongly keeled, disarticulating below the glumes, 2-4 mm long; glumes awnless, densely woolly, or villous all over, containing a single fertile floret; lemmas included within the glumes, short awned.

Plants perennial, rhizomatous; culms 1-8 dm tall, hollow, smooth, glabrous, decumbent; vernation rolled; sheaths open, smooth, glabrous; blades 2-5 mm wide, 5-15 cm long, flat, glabrous, scabrous adaxially and on edges, smooth abaxially; collars yellow, continuous or interrupted; auricles absent; ligules membranous, 1-3 mm long, truncate, erose, glabrous.

Inflorescence an ovoid or oblong panicle, woolly, 1-4 cm long, about 1 cm wide; spikelets woolly, 3-4 mm long; glumes woolly, same length as spikelets, 3-nerved; lemmas about as long as the glumes, glabrous below, awned from near the base, the awn geniculate and exserted slightly or as much as 5 mm beyond the glumes.

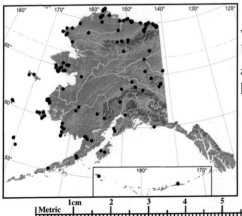

Native grass of moist to wet riparian meadows or tundra. Uncommon and found growing among sedges and willows during late August or early September.

Alpine foxtail
Tribe: Poeae

compressed panicle inflorescence

woolly spikelets

awn evident above glumes

floret

stigma

lemma awn

ligule

Shortawn foxtail
Alopecurus aequalis Sobol.

Perennial, tufted; membranous ligule; inflorescence an oblong or ovoid dense-spicate and cylindric panicle, less than 1 cm wide; spikelets strongly keeled, disarticulating below the glumes, 2-4 mm long; glumes awnless, villous on keel and nerves only, containing a single fertile floret; lemmas included within the glumes, short awned, awn exceeding the glumes by 1.5 mm or less.

Plants perennial, tufted; culms 1.5-6 dm tall, hollow, smooth, glabrous, erect or decumbent and rooting at nodes; vernation rolled; sheaths open, smooth, glabrous, inflated; blades 1-4 mm wide, 3-13 cm long, flat, glabrous, scaberulous or scaberulous on edges only; collars indistinct or yellow, constricted, interrupted; auricles absent; ligules membranous, 1.5-5 mm long, obtuse or acute, entire, glabrous.

Inflorescence a slender cylindrical panicle, 2-7 cm long, 4-5 mm wide; spikelets about 2 mm long; glumes same length as the spikelets, 3-nerved, ciliate, pilose on the nerves, pubescent to scabrous on the back; lemmas glabrous, about as long as the glumes, awned from below middle, straight or slightly geniculate, scarcely exserted (to about 1 mm beyond the glumes); anthers about 0.5 mm long.

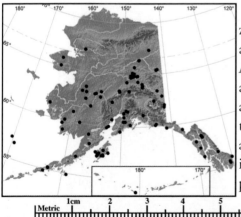

Native grass of riparian zones. Common in shallow water and wet newly deposited sediment. A colonizer eliminated by more aggressive tall sedges and grasses as habitat matures to meadows or tundra. Considered a weed in agriculture areas of Alaska where it often contaminates grass seed production.

Shortawn foxtail

Tribe: Poeae

anthers

stigma

anthers

lemma

spikelets

lemma awn

floret

compressed panicle inflorescence

ligule

Water foxtail

Alopecurus geniculatus L.

Perennial, tufted; membranous ligule; inflorescence an oblong or ovoid dense-spicate cylindric panicle, less than 1 cm wide; spikelets strongly keeled, disarticulating below the glumes, 2-4 mm long; glumes awnless, villous on keel and nerves only, containing a single fertile floret; lemmas included within the glumes, short awned, awn exceeding the glumes by 2 mm or more.

Plants perennial, tufted; culms 1.5-5 dm tall, hollow, smooth, glabrous, green or somewhat glaucous; vernation rolled; sheaths open, smooth, glabrous, inflated; blades 1-4 mm wide, 3-15 cm long, flat, glabrous, scaberulous to scabrous; collars yellow or purple, interrupted; auricles absent; ligules membranous, 1-4.2 mm long, obtuse or acute, entire or lacerate, glabrous.

Inflorescence a slender cylindrical panicle, 3-7 cm long, 4-5 mm wide; spikelets 2-3 mm long; glumes same length as spikelet, 3-nerved, pilose on nerves and sometimes pubescent on the back, the tip dark purple; lemmas about as long as glumes, glabrous or pubescent above on keel, awn from below middle, usually twisted at base and geniculate, exserted from 2-3 mm giving the panicle a bristly appearance.

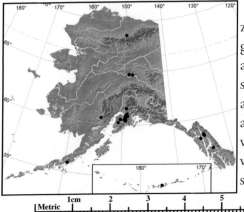

Native grass of riparian zones, which are wet most of the growing season. Uncommon and a colonizer of newly deposited sediments. Not competitive with aggressive riparian zone sedges and grasses. May be considered a weed in agriculture areas of Alaska where it often contaminates grass seed.

Water foxtail

Tribe: Poeae

compressed
panicle
inflorescence

ligule

lemma awn

awns
exceeding
the glumes

stigma

stigma

hairy glumes

floret

awnless
glumes

Circumpolar reedgrass
Calamagrostis deschampsioides Trin.

Perennial, rhizomatous, loosely tufted; inflorescence an open panicle at anthesis; culms to 6 dm tall, slender, usually smooth below the panicle; leaves to 15 cm long, to 3 mm wide, flat to somewhat involute; ligule membranous, to 3 mm long; spikelets with 1 fertile floret, reduced florets absent; glumes 4-5 mm long, rounded, sometimes scabrous on the midvein; callus conspicuously hairy with hairs of mixed length, 0.4-0.7 times as long as the lemma; lemma included within the glumes, awn from just below the middle of the lemma, exserted, rarely included within the glumes, slender, twisted, weakly to strongly bent.

Plants perennial, rhizomatous, loosely tufted; culms to 6 dm tall, unbranched, smooth below the panicles; ligules to 3 mm long; leaf blades usually 3-8 cm long, 1-3 mm wide, flat to somewhat involute.

Panicle to 12 cm long, 4.5 cm wide, pyramidal, open, erect; spikelets usually confined to the distal ½ of the branches; spikelets to 7 mm long, rachilla prolongations 1-2 mm long; glumes rounded, mostly smooth, apices acute to acuminate; callus hairs of mixed length, 0.4-0.7 times as long as the lemmas, abundant; lemmas to 5 mm long, shorter than the glumes; awns to 5.5 mm long, from the lower ⅓-½ of the lemma, usually exserted, distinguishable from the callus hairs, weakly to strongly bent.

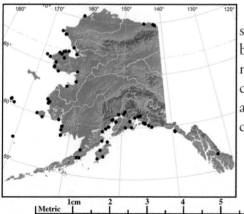

Native grass tolerant of saline conditions along coastal beaches and brackish coastal marshes. Appears to be a colonizer and replaced by other aggressive sedges and grasses as coastal meadows develop.

Circumpolar reedgrass

Tribe: Poeae

open panicle inflorescence

ligule

awn long
and twisted

panicle
branch

spikelets

floret

floret

lemma

palea

callus hairs
shorter than the lemma

glumes

glumes

Purple reedgrass
Calamagrostis purpurascens R. Br.

Perennial, densely tufted, sometimes with short rhizomes; inflorescence an appressed and spicate panicle; ligule membranous; spikelets with 1 fertile floret, reduced florets absent; lemma included within the glumes, callus conspicuously hairy; geniculate awn from the middle of the lemmas, longer than the glumes, 4.5-9 mm long.

Plants perennial, densely tufted; culms 2-6 dm tall, hollow, smooth, glabrous; vernation rolled; sheaths open, smooth, glabrous; blades 2-4 mm wide, 4-10 cm long, flat or involute, smooth and pubescent adaxially, pubescent below and smooth or scaberulous abaxially, edges scabrous; collars minutely puberulent at sides; auricles absent; ligules membranous, 3-5 mm long, obtuse, lacerate, puberulent abaxially.

Panicle 5-12 cm long, dense and more or less spikelike, often interrupted below, pale green or purplish; spikelets 5-7 mm long; glumes subequal, scabrous on the keel, acuminate, 1-nerved on the first, somewhat 3-nerved on the second; lemmas 4-5 mm long, the apex with 4 setaceous teeth, callus hairs about 1.2-1.5 mm long, the awn from near the base, twisted and straight until near the end of the lemma, then geniculate, 4.5-9 mm long; rachilla hairs 1-1.5 mm long, sometimes shorter.

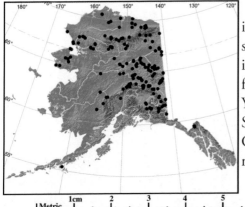

Native grass usually found in dry rocky sites with shallow soils. In tundra, it appears to be isolated to dry hummocks. Not found in the wetter regions of the Yukon Delta or Southcentral and Southeastern Alaska. Commercially produced for reclamation projects.

Purple reedgrass
Tribe: Poeae

hairy on adaxial side of leaf

spikelet

lemma

palea

awn longer than glumes

long geniculate awns

palea

ligule

glumes

florets with basal tuft of hair

One-and-a-half-flowered reedgrass
Calamagrostis sesquiflora (Trin.) Tzvelev
C. purpurascens subsp. *arctica* (Vasey) Hultén

Perennial, densely tufted, sometimes with short rhizomes; inflorescence an appressed and spicate panicle; ligule membranous; spikelets with 1 fertile floret, reduced florets absent; lemma included within the glumes, callus conspicuously hairy; awns stout and bent from the lower part of the lemmas, longer than the glumes, usually 7-11 mm long.

Plants perennial, densely tufted, sometimes with short rhizomes; culms to 5 dm tall, unbranched; sheaths and collars smooth; blades to 31 cm long, 7 mm wide, flat, abaxial surfaces scabrous, adaxial surfaces smooth to slightly scabrous to sparsely hairy; ligules to 6 mm long, usually entire.

Panicle inflorescence erect, contracted to somewhat open, usually purple tinged; branches 1.5-3 cm long, usually scabrous; spikelet bearing to the base; spikelets to about 9 mm long; glumes keeled, scabrous the whole length, usually acuminate and twisted distally; 1 fertile floret, lemma shorter than the glumes, to 6 mm long, callus hairs to 3 mm long, awns usually 7-11 mm long, stout, attached near the base of the lemma, bent, and exserted more than 2 mm.

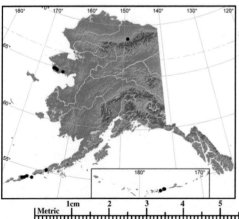

Native grass uncommon and isolated to drier coastal habitats with shallow soils.

92

One-and-a-half-flowered reedgrass
Tribe: Poeae

panicle

panicle branch

ligule

stout lemma awn

scabrous keel of glumes

glumes

spikelet

callus with tuft of hairs

leaf abaxial side scabrous and not hairy

Pacific reedgrass
Calamagrostis nutkaensis (J. Presl) Steud.

Perennial, densely tufted, rhizomes short; inflorescence an appressed or contracted panicle at anthesis; culms tall, 3-4 mm thick at base; leaves to 2 cm wide; ligule membranous; spikelets with 1 fertile floret, reduced florets absent; glumes to 8 mm long, keeled, smooth, sometimes scabrous on the keel, apex acuminate; lemma included within the glumes, 4-5 mm long, lemma awns not exserted; callus conspicuously hairy, hairs of mixed length, ½ the length of the lemma.

Plants perennial, densely tufted, short rhizomes; culms to 15 dm tall, stout, unbranched, 3-4 mm thick at base; leaf blades to 56 cm long, 2 cm wide, flat, usually erect; ligule membranous, to 5.5 mm long, often hidden by an expanded collar.

Panicle appressed or contracted and somewhat nodding at anthesis, to 33 cm long, 9 cm wide; branches to 10 cm long, spikelets usually confined to the distal ½; spikelets to 8 mm long; glumes keeled, smooth, infrequently scabrous on the keels, apices acuminate; callus hairs 0.5-0.7 times as long as the lemmas, sparse; lemmas 4-5 mm long, awned from below the middle, not exserted, easily distinguished from the callus hairs, usually straight.

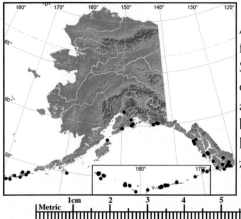

Native grass of the Aleutian Islands and coastal forests of Southcentral and Southeastern Alaska. Often found on fresh and salt water sand dunes and beaches. This robust grass is being commercialized for seed to help revegetate disturbed riparian zones and ocean shorelines.

94

Pacific reedgrass

Tribe: Poeae

panicle inflorescence

scabrous glumes along full length

rather stiff and robust lemma awn

narrow panicle inflorescence

lemma awn

ligule

spikelets with stiff appressed branches

florets

callus hairs not more than one half the length of the lemma

spikelet with long glumes

Bluejoint reedgrass
Calamagrostis canadensis var. *langsdorffii* (Link) Inman

Perennial, rhizomatous, loosely tufted; culms slender; inflorescence an open and loose panicle at anthesis; branches 2.7-12 cm long; ligule membranous; spikelets with 1 fertile floret, 4-4.5 mm long, reduced florets absent; glumes 4-6 mm long, narrow, distinctly acuminate, very scabrous on the keel and elsewhere; lemma included within the glumes, 2-4 mm long; callus conspicuously hairy, hairs about the same length, usually longer than the lemma; awns usually straight, included or slightly longer than the glumes, inconspicuous and delicate.

Plants perennial, rhizomatous, loosely tufted; culms to 18 dm tall, slender, often branching above the base; ligules membranous, to 12 mm long; leaf blades to 50 cm long, 11 mm wide, flat, lax, adaxial surfaces usually scabrous.

Panicle inflorescence to 25 cm long, 8 cm wide, often contracted when immature, open and nodding when mature; branches 2.7-12 cm long, scabrous, spikelets concentrated on the distal ⅔; spikelets 4-4.5 mm long; glumes acuminate, very scabrous on the keel and elsewhere, exceeding a single fertile floret, 4-6 mm long; callus hairs usually 1-1.2 times as long as the lemmas, abundant, awn attached near the base of the lemma, usually not exserted, delicate, difficult to distinguish from the callus hairs, usually straight.

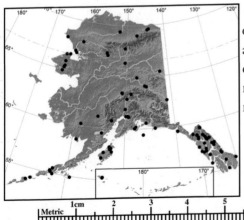

Native grass common to open meadows, open forested areas, willow thickets, and shores of lakes, ponds, and bogs. A robust grass common in all regions of Alaska.

Bluejoint reedgrass

Tribe: Poeae

panicle branch

large nodding inflorescence

spikelets

floret

callus hairs much longer than lemma

ligule

floret awn

floret

narrow glumes

97

Bluejoint reedgrass
Calamagrostis canadensis (Michx.) P. Beauv. var. *canadensis*

Perennial, rhizomatous, loosely tufted; culms slender; inflorescence an open and loose panicle at anthesis; branches 2.9-5.7 cm long; ligule membranous; spikelets with 1 fertile floret, 2.5-4 mm long, reduced florets absent; glumes to 4 mm long, somewhat rounded, acute at the apex, seldom acuminate, somewhat scabrous on the keel, little elsewhere; lemma included within the glumes; callus conspicuously hairy, hairs about the same length, usually longer than the lemma; awns usually straight but may be somewhat twisted, included or slightly longer than the glumes, inconspicuous.

Plants perennial, rhizomatous, loosely tufted; culms to 16 dm tall, slender, often branching above the base; ligules membranous, to 12 mm long; leaf blades to 41 cm long, 8 mm wide, flat, lax, adaxial surfaces usually scabrous.

Panicle inflorescence to 19 cm long, 7 cm wide, often contracted when immature, open and nodding when mature; branches 2.9-5.7 cm long, scabrous, spikelets concentrated on the distal ⅔; spikelets to 4 mm long; glumes, rounded to slightly keeled, rarely acuminate, often scabrous only on the keel, exceeding a single fertile floret; callus hairs 0.9-1.1 times as long as the lemmas, abundant, awn attached near the base of the lemma, usually not exserted, delicate, difficult to distinguish from the callus hairs, usually straight.

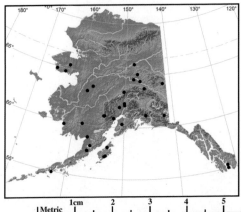

Native grass common to open meadows, tundra, forested areas, willows, and shores of lakes, ponds, and bogs. Not as robust as *C. canadensis* var. *langsdorffii,* but still very common in Alaska south of the Arctic Circle. The cultivar 'Sourdough' has been released for revegetation of disturbed areas.

98

Bluejoint reedgrass
Tribe: Poeae

ligule

open panicle branch
spikelets

lemma straight awn

glumes

basal tuft of hair

Lapland reedgrass
Calamagrostis lapponica (Wahlenb.) Hartm.

Perennial, rhizomatous, tufted; inflorescence a soft appressed or contracted panicle at anthesis; culms slender; leaves narrow, soft; ligule membranous, 2-4 mm long; spikelets with 1 fertile floret, reduced florets absent; glumes 4-5.5 mm long, rounded to slightly keeled, slightly scabrous on the keel, apex acute to acuminate; lemma included within the glumes, callus conspicuously hairy with hairs of mixed length, longest hairs as long to just longer than the length of the lemma, awn from below the middle of the lemma, not exserted.

Plants perennial, rhizomatous, tufted; culms up to 9 dm tall, slender, smooth, glabrous; sheaths open, smooth, glabrous; ligules 2-4 mm long; blades to 26 cm long, 4 mm wide, flat to involute.

Panicle to 16 cm long, narrow, erect, loosely contracted, purple, sometimes spikelet-bearing to the base; branches 2.1-5.4 cm long; spikelets 3.5-5.5 mm long; glumes usually more than 3 times as long as wide, rounded to slightly keeled, apices acute to acuminate; lemmas shorter than the glumes, callus hairs of mixed length, the longest 0.8-1.2 times as long as the lemmas; lemma awns attached below the middle, delicate, straight, about as long as lemma, 1.5-3 mm long, not exserted.

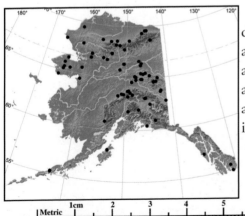

Native grass common to drier well drained soils of alpine and arctic tundra. Common along short shrub covered ridges and slopes. Loosely tufted, and although common never present in great quantities.

100

Lapland reedgrass

Tribe: Poeae

spikelets
of branch

appressed panicle inflorescence

glumes

spikelets

lemma awns

florets

ligule

callus hairs
as long as
lemma

Northern reedgrass

Calamagrostis stricta subsp. *inexpansa* (A. Gray) C.W. Greene
Calamagrostis inexpansa A. Gray

Perennial, rhizomatous, tufted; inflorescence an appressed or contracted panicle with stiff branches, at anthesis 1.5-9.5 cm long; culms slender, usually scabrous; leaves narrow, stiff; ligule membranous, 6 mm long; spikelets with 1 fertile floret, reduced florets absent; glumes 3-5 mm long, keeled, scabrous on the keel, apex acute; rachilla prolongation 1-1.5 mm long; lemma included within the glumes, callus conspicuously hairy and hairs of mixed length, longest hairs just shorter than the length of the lemma, awn from below the middle of the lemma.

Plants perennial, rhizomatous; culms up to 12 dm tall, mostly scabrous; sheaths open, smooth, glabrous; ligules 2-6 mm long, blades to 34 cm long, 6 mm wide, usually involute.

Panicle to 29 cm long, narrow, dense, more or less lobed, branches mostly erect, spikelet-bearing to the base, pale green or purplish, 1.5-9 cm long; spikelets to 5 mm long; glumes usually less than 3 times as long as wide, rounded or keeled, usually smooth, keels smooth or scabrous, apices acute; rachilla about the length of lemma 1-1.5 mm long; callus hairs of mixed length, 0.7-1.3 times as long as lemma; lemmas shorter than the glumes, awn attached below the middle of the lemma, straight or somewhat bent.

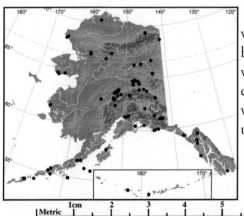

Native grass common to wet tundra, bogs, and other moist habitat. Common along open water of tundra, ponds and lake edges, often growing in standing water. Very rhizomatous and not usually present in great quantities.

Northern reedgrass
Tribe: Poeae

panicle branch

lemma awn

palea

lemma awn

lemma awn

spikelets

lower glume

upper glume

callus and tuft of hair

lemma

pubescent leaf blade

lower glume

lemma awn

ligule

Slimstem reedgrass

Calamagrostis stricta (Timm) Koeler subsp. *stricta*

C. neglecta (Ehrh.) P. Gaertn., *C. hólmii* Lange in Holm

Perennial, rhizomatous, tufted; inflorescence an appressed or contracted panicle with stiff branches, at anthesis 1.4-4 cm long; culms slender, usually scabrous; leaves narrow, stiff; ligule membranous, to 6 mm long; spikelets with 1 fertile floret, reduced florets absent; glumes 3-5 mm long, keeled, scabrous on the keel, apex acute; rachilla prolongation 0.5-1 mm long; lemma included within the glumes, callus conspicuously hairy and hairs of mixed length, longest hairs just shorter than the length of the lemma, awn from below the middle of the lemma.

Plants perennial, rhizomatous; culms up to 10 dm tall, mostly scabrous; sheaths open, smooth, glabrous; ligules to 6 mm long, blades to 25 cm long, 3 mm wide, usually involute.

Panicle appressed or contracted, sometimes interrupted, to 13 cm long, 3 cm wide, somewhat lobed; branches 1.4-4 cm long; spikelets crowded, extending nearly to the base of the branches, 2-2.5 mm long; glumes keeled; rachilla prolongation 0.5-1 mm long; callus hairs of mixed length, distinctly shorter than the lemma, usually 0.7-0.8 times as long as the lemma; lemmas shorter than the glumes, awn attached below the middle of the lemma, straight or somewhat bent.

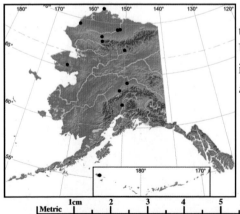

Native grass of moist tundra. Favors fine textured soils. Uncommon and usually mistaken in the field as *C. stricta* subsp. *inexpansa*.

Slimstem reedgrass
Tribe: Poeae

contracted panicle inflorescence

spikelets

leaf blades

ligule

anthers

palea

lemma

lemma awn

glumes

lemma

florets

spikelet

Drooping woodreed
Cinna latifolia (Trevir. ex Göpp.) Griseb.

Rhizomatous; inflorescence a well exserted and open-panicle, branches and spikelets often drooping; ligule membranous; spikelets with 1 fertile floret, reduced florets absent, disarticulating below the glumes; glumes about 2.5-4 mm long, longer than the single floret; callus glabrous; lemma short awned from just below the apex; palea as long as the lemma.

Plants perennial, rhizomatous; culms up to 15 dm tall, smooth or scabrous; sheaths open, glabrous, scaberulous; blades up to 15 mm wide, flat, glabrous, scabrous; collars yellowish or brownish, continuous; auricles absent; ligules membranous, 3-8 mm long, truncate, lacerate, glabrous.

Panicle 12-30 cm long, open, spreading or drooping; spikelets 1-flowered, about 4 mm long, disarticulating below the glumes, the rachilla extended beyond the palea as a minute bristle; glumes subequal, 2.5-4 mm long, 1-nerved; callus glabrous; lemma shorter than the glumes, the awn 1 mm long, from the back just below the apex; palea 2-nerved, the nerves very close together.

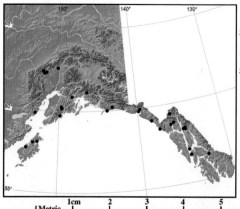

Native grass occurring along shaded streams, trails and roads of late-seral coastal forests and riparian zones.

Drooping woodreed
Tribe: Poeae

palea

lemma

spikelets

florets

open panicle
inflorescence

ligule

Arctic bent

Podagrostis aequivalvis (Trin.) Scribn. & Merr.

Agrostis aequivalvis Trin.

Rhizomatous; inflorescence an open-panicle, branches and spikelets often drooping; ligule membranous; spikelet 2.3-4.3 mm long, glumes longer than the single fertile floret; florets disarticulating above the glumes, reduced florets absent; callus glabrous; palea well developed, at least half as long as the single lemma, 2-veined; rachilla prolongations 0.5-1.9 mm long.

Plants perennial, rhizomatous; culms to 90 dm, erect; sheaths smooth; ligule membranous, to 0.4-4 mm long; leaf blades to 18 cm long, 3.5 mm wide, flat.

Panicles open, ovate, often drooping, sparsely branched, 1-5 branches at the lowest nodes, usually scabridulous, spikelets usually restricted to the distal 1/2; spikelets ovate to lanceolate, 1 fertile floret, reduced florets absent; glumes longer than the lemma; palea well developed, 2-veined; rachilla prolongations 0.5-1.9 mm long.

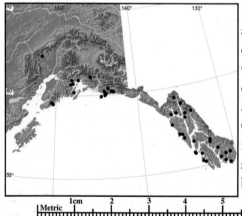

Native riparian grass found along streams, lakes, and bogs in coastal spruce-hemlock forests. Common to Southeast Alaska, the coastal regions of Prince William Sound, and Southcentral Alaska. Often overlooked in meadows as it is delicate and the spikelets are small and few on scattered branches.

Arctic bent

Tribe: Poeae

branches

open panicle inflorescence

spikelets

anther

stigma

ligule

palea

glumes

florets

lemma

lemma

palea

palea

distal end of
rachilla hairy

lemma

long rachilla

rachilla

Alpine bent; Snow bent

Podagrostis humilis (Vasey) Björkman

P. thurberiana (Hitchc.) Hultén, *Agrostis humilis* Vasey

Plants tufted, sometimes rhizomatous; inflorescence an open-panicle, generally short and deltoid; ligule membranous; spikelets 1.6-2.3 mm long, longer than the single fertile floret; florets disarticulating above the glumes, reduced florets absent; callus glabrous; palea well developed, at least half as long as the single lemma, 2-veined; rachilla prolongations 0.1-0.6 mm long.

Plants perennial, tufted, sometimes rhizomatous; culms to 0.5-5 dm tall, smooth, glabrous; blades 2-15 cm long, 1-4 mm wide, flat or involute; ligules membranous, 0.5-3.2 mm long.

Panicles open, narrow to deltoid, sparsely branched, smooth or scabridulous, spikelets usually restricted to the distal 1/2; spikelets ovate to lanceolate, 1 fertile floret, reduced florets absent; glumes longer than the lemma; node branches mostly 1-4 below, 2's or single above, erect or slightly spreading, spikelet-bearing beyond the middle; spikelets 1.6-2.3 mm long; glumes somewhat equal, palea well developed, 2-veined; rachilla prolongations 0.1-0.6 mm long.

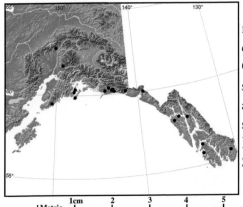

Native grass of alpine riparian meadows associated with coastal spruce-hemlock forests. Occupies sediments along streambanks, bogs, pond edges, and lakeshores where other grasses, sedges, or rushes are not prevalent. Flowers in late August and early September.

Alpine bent; Snow bent
Tribe: Poeae

panicle inflorescence

lemma shorter than glumes

floret

spikelets

glumes

anther 0.5 mm long

florets

prolonged rachilla

ligule

branch

Redtop bentgrass

Agrostis stolonifera L.
Agrostis alba L.

Perennial, tufted to mat forming, stoloniferous, stolons 5-100+ cm, rooting at the nodes; inflorescence a panicle that is narrowly contracted, dense, and somewhat open at anthesis, branches spikelet-bearing nearly to the base, to 7 branches at the lower nodes; ligule membranous; spikelets with 1 fertile floret, reduced florets absent, disarticulating above the glumes; glumes to 3 mm long, longer than the single floret; callus minutely hairy, hairs 0.5 mm long; palea at least ⅖ as long as the lemma, not veined.

Plants perennial, tufted to mat forming, stoloniferous, perennial; culms to 6 dm tall, often geniculate at the base; often rooting at lower nodes; leaves mostly cauline; ligule to 7.5 mm long; blades to 10 cm long, 6 mm wide, flat.

Panicle to 20 cm long, 6 cm wide, dense, appressed to open at anthesis, less than ½ the length of the culm; branches scabrous, spikelet-bearing very nearly to the base, most numerous in the lower whorls; glumes subequal, to 3 mm long, acute to acuminate, scabrous to scabridulous over the midvein; lemmas about ¾ the length of the glumes, callus minutely pubescent, veins usually excurrent about the middle as a minute prickle or as a short awn scarcely exceeding the tip of the lemma; palea at least ⅖ as long as the lemma, not veined.

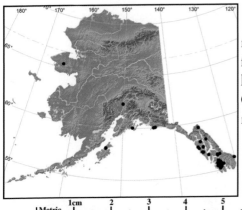

Introduced grass of moist riparian zones. A traditional forage grass of meadows, but has had limited use in Alaska. Occasionally used in the past for reclamation of disturbed areas.

Redtop bentgrass
Tribe: Poeae

floret

glumes

panicle / inflorescence

palea

lemma

floret

palea

ligule

spikelet

spikelets

Redtop
Agrostis gigantea Roth

Perennial, rhizomatous, sometimes rooting at the lower nodes of the culm; inflorescence an erect, open ovate panicle; lower branches spikelet-bearing nearly to the base, to 8 branches at the lower nodes; ligule membranous; spikelets with 1 fertile floret, reduced florets absent, disarticulating above the glumes; spikelets ovate to lanceolate; glumes to 3.2 mm long, longer than the single floret; callus minutely hairy, hairs 0.5 mm long; palea at least ⅖ as long as the lemma, not veined.

Plants perennial, rhizomatous, rhizomes to 25 cm; culms to 12 dm tall, erect to geniculate at the base, sometimes rooting at the lower nodes; leaves mostly cauline, blades to 10 cm long, 8 mm wide; ligule membranous, to 7 mm long.

Panicle to 30 cm long, 15 cm wide, erect, open, broadly ovate, less than ½ the length of the culm; branches scabrous, spikelet-bearing very nearly to the base, most numerous in the lower whorls; spikelets narrowly ovate to lanceolate; glumes subequal, to 3.2 mm long, lanceolate, scabrous to scabridulous over the midvein; lemmas to 2.2 mm long; callus minutely pubescent, lemma usually not awned, if awned, awn to 3 mm long; palea at least ⅖ as long as the lemma, not veined.

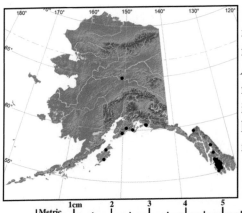

Introduced grass of moist riparian zones, roadsides, and forest borders. As with *A. stolonifera*, it is a common forage grass of meadows elsewhere in the world, but has seen only limited use as a forage and revegetation grass in Alaska.

Redtop
Tribe: *Poeae*

open panicle inflorescence

ligule

panicle branch

florets

lemmas

floret

palea 1/2 the length of the lemma

glumes

spikelets

115

Colonial bent; Browntop; Rhode Island bent

Agrostis capillaris L.

Agrostis tenuis Sibth.

Perennial, rhizomatous, rhizomes to 5 cm long; inflorescence an open panicle, branches naked at the base, spikelets usually confined to the distal ½ of the branches, to 9 branches at the lower nodes; ligule membranous; spikelets with 1 fertile floret, reduced florets absent, disarticulating above the glumes; glumes to 3 mm long, longer than the single floret; callus mostly glabrous, few hairs 0.1mm long; palea at least ⅖ as long as the lemma, not veined.

Plants perennial, rhizomatous; culms to 7.5 dm tall, erect or geniculate; leaves basal and cauline, to 10 cm long, 5 mm wide, flat; ligules membranous, to 2 mm long.

Panicle to 20 cm long, delicate, the whorls composed of up to 13 branches, mostly long and slender, unbranched and naked towards the base, spikelets confined to distal ½; spikelets lanceolate or oblong; glumes subequal, to 3 mm long, smooth to scabridulous on the midvein; lemma thin, ¾ as long as the glumes, rarely awned; callus glabrous or minutely hairy, hairs to 0.1 mm long; palea usually at least ⅖ the length of the lemma, not veined.

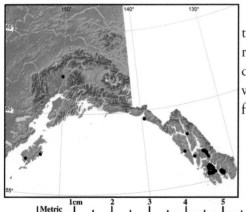

Introduced grass known to occupy the drier area of riparian zones, forest borders, and disturbed areas. May be included with commercial seed sources used for lawns.

Colonial bent; Browntop; Rhode Island bent

branch spikelets

branches naked at the base

lemma

open panicle inflorescence

palea usually about 2/5 as long as lemma

florets

spikelet

ligule

Spike bent

Agrostis exarata Trin.

Agrostis alaskana Hultén

Perennial, tufted; panicle narrow, contracted, lobed, at least some branches floriferous to the base; membranous ligule; glumes subequal, about 2-4 mm long, longer than the single fertile floret, reduced floret absent, disarticulation above the glumes; callus glabrous; palea obsolete or much less than half as long as the lemma.

Plants perennial, tufted; culms to 10 dm tall; blades to 20 cm long, 7 mm wide, flat; ligules membranous, to 11 mm long, obtuse, entire or lacerate, glabrous.

Panicle 30 cm long, contracted, sometimes almost spikelike, more often lobed, especially the lowest whorls, the branches strongly scabrous, at least some branches floriferous to the base; glumes subequal, 2-4 mm long, acute, scabrous on the back and keel; lemma ⅔ the length of the glumes, 5-nerved, the nerves minutely scabrous towards the tip, the midnerve occasionally excurrent as a minute prickle; callus glabrous; palea absent or less than 0.5 mm long.

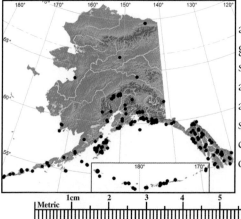

Native riparian grass associated with mineral soils, gravels, sands, and sediments of streambanks, meander point bars, and exposed riffles. Often found along silty beaches and coastal sand dunes. May be considered a colonizer, and is crowded out by other aggressive grasses and sedges.

Spike bent

spikelets

spicate
panicle
inflorescence

glumes

anther

florets

lemma
and
no palea

ligule

ligule

119

Northern bent

Agrostis mertensii Trin.

Agrostis borealis Hartm.

Perennial, tufted not rhizomatous; panicle somewhat contracted but more open at anthesis; branches mostly naked towards the base, erect, not capillary; ligule membranous; glumes subequal, about 2-4 mm long, longer than the single fertile floret, reduced floret absent, disarticulation above the glumes; lemma awned from just below the midpoint, to 4.4 mm long, geniculate, exserted, persistent; callus hairs present, sparse, 0.4 mm long; palea obsolete or to 0.1 mm long; anthers 0.5-0.8 mm long.

Plants perennial, tufted; culms to 4 dm tall, erect; leaves mostly basal and persistent, blades to 13 cm long, 3 mm wide, flat; ligules to 3.3 mm long.

Panicle spreading, to 10 cm long, 5 cm wide, lower branches whorled and spreading, exserted from the upper sheaths at maturity, lowest node with 2-5 branches, branches visible, not capillary, naked near the base; spikelets lanceolate; glumes subequal, 2-4 mm long; a single floret, reduced florets absent; lemmas to 2.6 mm long, awned from just below middle, awns to 4.4 mm long, geniculate, exserted, persistent; palea absent, or 0.1 mm and thin; anthers 0.5-0.8 mm long.

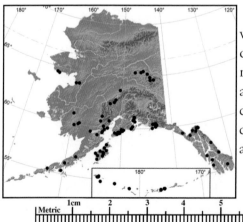

Native riparian grass of well-drained gravel bars and disturbed areas of streams and rivers. Also occupies well-drained areas of rocky alpine areas and cliffs, as well as, rocky and gravelly coasts. Often confused with the awned form of *A. scabra*.

Northern bent

Tribe: Poeae

spikelets

panicle branch

spikelets

geniculate awn

panicle inflorescence

floret and stamens

stamens

lemma

ovary

glumes

ligule

reduced palea

121

Brown bent

Agrostis vinealis Schreb.

Agrostis trinii Turcz.

Perennial, tufted, rhizomatous; panicle somewhat contracted but more open at anthesis; branches mostly naked towards the base, erect, not capillary; ligule membranous; glumes subequal, about 2-4 mm long, longer than the single fertile floret, reduced floret absent, disarticulation above the glumes; lemma awned from just below the midpoint, awns to 4.5 mm long, geniculate, exserted, persistent; callus hairs present, sparse, 0.4 mm long; palea to 0.2 mm long; anthers 0.7-1.8 mm long.

Plants perennial, tufted, rhizomatous; culms to 6 dm tall, erect or geniculate at the base; leaves mostly basal and persistent, blades to 10 cm long, 3 mm wide, flat; ligules to 5 mm long.

Panicle spreading, to 15 cm long, 8 cm wide, lower branches whorled and spreading, exserted from the upper sheaths at maturity, lowest node with 3-8 branches, branches visible and not capillary, naked near the base; spikelets lanceolate to narrowly oblong; glumes subequal, to 4 mm long; a single floret, reduced florets absent; lemmas to 2.4 mm long, awned from about the base, awns to 4.5 mm long, geniculate, exserted, persistent; palea to 0.2 mm long and thin; anthers 0.7-1.8 mm long.

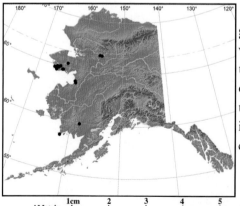

Appears to be a native grass occupying dry rocky and well-drained soils of the dry tundra near Nome and a few other similar locations. Known to be native to Europe, but there is some question as to whether it is circumpolar and native to Alaska.

Brown bent
Tribe: Poeae

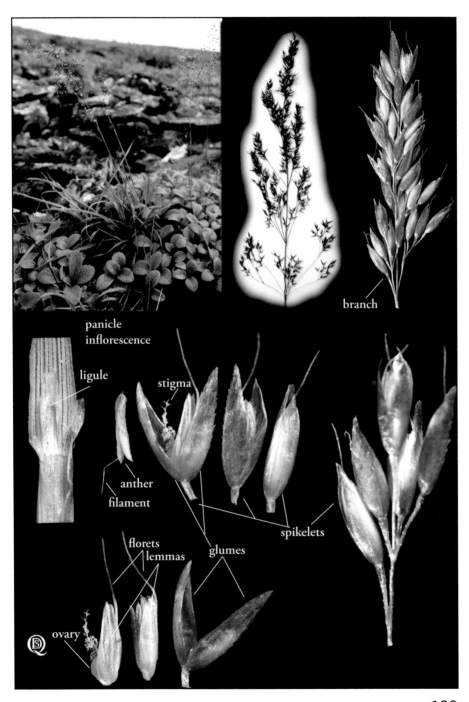

panicle
inflorescence

branch

ligule

stigma

anther

filament

florets

lemmas

glumes

spikelets

ovary

Winter bent
Agrostis scabra Willd.

Perennial, tufted, not rhizomatous or stoloniferous; leaf blades to 2 mm wide; panicle open diffuse, usually as wide as long at anthesis; branches mostly naked towards the base, erect, capillary, scabrous, to 12 cm long; ligule membranous, up to 5 mm long; glumes unequal, to 3.4 mm long, longer than the single fertile floret, reduced floret absent, disarticulation above the glumes; lemma awned or unawned, if awned, awn from just below the midpoint, to 2.5 mm long, straight or geniculate, persistent, usually not exserted; callus hairs sparse, 0.2 mm long; palea absent or to 0.2 mm long; anthers to 0.8 mm long.

Plants perennial, tufted, not rhizomatous; culms to 9 dm tall, erect; blades 14 cm long, 2 mm wide, basal blades involute, cauline blades flat; ligules membranous, 5 mm long.

Panicle to 50 cm long, 20 cm wide, open, diffuse, branches in whorls, bearing spikelets near the ends, the basal ones not branching until ⅔ from the base; spikelets to 3.4 mm long; glumes nearly unequal, long-acuminate, scabrous on the 1 nerve; lemma ⅔ the length of the glumes, awnless, or awned in *Agrostis scabra* var. *geminata*, slightly bearded on the callus; palea minute or absent.

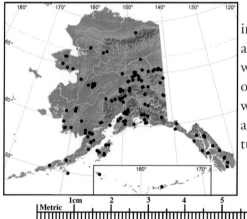

Native grass. Common in disturbed areas like clear cuts and roadsides. Also found in well-drained gravel bars and banks of rivers. Present on forest floors where light penetrates the canopy and in well-drained and dry tundra.

Winter bent
Tribe: Poeae

spikelets

diffuse panicle inflorescence

ligule

A. scabra var. geminata

awn

florets

anthers

floret

spikelet

ovary

obsolete or small palea

glumes

spikelet

125

Clavate bent
Agrostis clavata Trin.

Annual or short-lived perennial, tufted, not rhizomatous or stoloniferous; leaf blades up to 7 mm wide; panicle open diffuse, longer than wide at anthesis; branches mostly naked towards the base, erect, capillary, scabrous, to 12 cm long; ligule membranous, to 4.2 mm long; glumes subequal, to 2.8 mm long, longer than the single fertile floret, reduced floret absent, disarticulation above the glumes; lemma unawned; callus hairs sparse, 0.2 mm long, sometimes glabrous; palea absent or to 0.2 mm long; anthers 0.3-0.6 mm long.

Plants annual or short lived, tufted, not rhizomatous or stoloniferous; culms to 7 dm long; leaves mostly basal, to 20 cm long, 7 mm wide, flat; ligules up to 4.2 mm long.

Panicles open, to 35 cm long, 10 cm wide, usually exserted, sometimes enclosed in the sheaths at maturity, widely ovate, lax; branches to 8 at the lowest node, spikelet bearing on the distal ½, pedicels to 5.5 mm long, clavate; spikelets to 2.8 mm long; glumes subequal, acute to acuminate; callus hairs sparse to 0.2 mm long; lemmas unawned; paleas absent or up to 0.2 mm long, anthers 0.3-0.6 mm long.

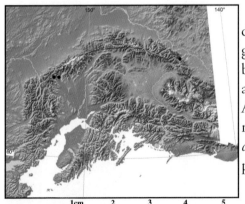

Native grass found on disturbed areas like sand and gravel bars, meadows, and forest borders. Uncommon in Alaska and appears restricted to the Alaska Range. Likely to be mistaken for *A. scabra,* but *A. clavata* leaves are wider and the pedicels clavate.

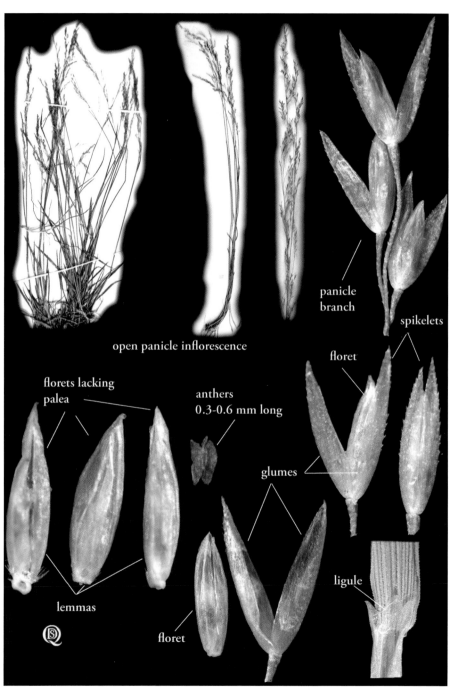

panicle branch

spikelets

open panicle inflorescence

floret

florets lacking palea

anthers 0.3-0.6 mm long

glumes

lemmas

floret

ligule

American sloughgrass

Beckmannia syzigachne (Steud.) Fernald

Plants perennial; inflorescence a panicle of racemes; membranous ligule; spikelets sessile in 2 rows, 1-sided, the spicate branches arranged on the panicle branches to form racemes; glumes longer than usually 1 single floret, sometimes 2; glumes inflated; disarticulates below the glumes when mature.

Plants perennial; culms to 12 dm tall; blades to 5 mm wide, flat; ligules membranous, 4-6 mm long.

Inflorescence a narrow, more or less interrupted panicle, to 30 cm long; spikelets usually 1-perfect floret, sometimes a second undeveloped or well-developed floret present, laterally compressed, nearly sessile and closely imbricate, in 2 rows along one side of short spicate branches, disarticulating below the glumes; glumes 2-3 mm long, equal, inflated, obovate, 3-nerved, rounded above, but the apex apiculate; lemmas narrow, 2.5-3.5 mm long, 5-nerved; palea nearly as long as the lemma.

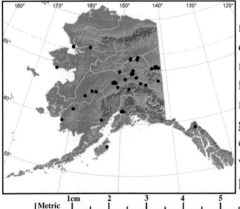

Native grass of wet riparian zones. A colonizer of deposited sediment along roadways and along margins of freshwater lakes, ponds, marshes, wet meadows, and lower gradient streams. The Alaska cultivar release 'Egan' is used for wetland reseedings and some pasture development.

American sloughgrass
Tribe: Poeae

raceme branches and spikelets

ligule

floret

spikelets

inflated glumes

Sweet vernalgrass; Sweetgrass
Anthoxanthum odoratum L.

Perennial, tufted; rhizomes short; appressed or compressed panicle inflorescence; spikelets with 1 perfect and 2 sterile florets, sterile from below and somewhat level with the fertile floret on each side, all looking alike; glumes unequal, not inflated and the upper usually including all lemmas; sterile florets distinctly awned, awns of the upper staminate florets to 9 mm long.

Plants perennial, tufted, rhizomes if present short; culms up to 10 dm tall, erect, simple or sparingly branched; leaf blades up to 31 cm long, to 10 mm wide; ligule to 7 mm long.

Panicle to 14 cm long, 2.5 cm wide, appressed to compressed, spikelets congested, lower branches pubescent; spikelets to 10 mm long; glumes unequal, lower to 4 mm, upper 10 mm long; 2 sterile florets to 4 mm long, awn of the lower to 4 mm and the upper to 9 mm long, equaling or slightly exceeding the upper glumes, fertile florets to 2.5 mm long and centered between the 2 sterile florets of each spikelet.

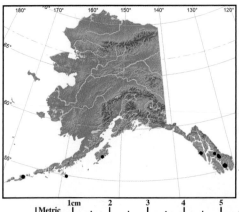

An introduced grass used to add fragrance to forage in Europe, but unpalatable to farm animals because of its bitter taste. Appears to be eliminating grass species on coastal bluffs in southern British Columbia, but its invasive nature is unknown in Alaska.

Sweet vernalgrass; Sweetgrass
Tribe: Poeae

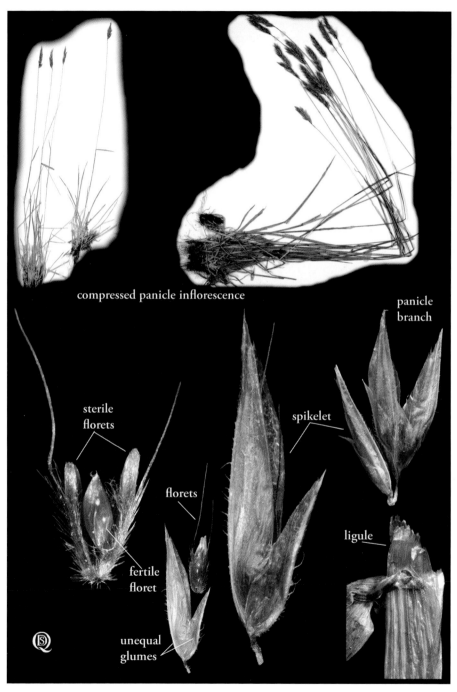

compressed panicle inflorescence

panicle branch

sterile florets

spikelet

florets

fertile floret

ligule

unequal glumes

Alpine sweetgrass

Anthoxanthum monticola subsp. *alpinum* (Sw. *ex* Willd.) Soreng
Hierochloë alpina (Sw. *ex* Willd.) Roem. & Schult.

Perennial, somewhat tufted; rhizomatous, rhizomes short; appressed panicle inflorescence; spikelets with 1 perfect and 2 staminate florets, staminate from below and level with the fertile floret on each side, all looking alike; glumes subequal, not inflated and about including all lemmas; staminate florets distinctly awned, awns of the upper staminate florets to 10.5 mm long.

Plants perennial, tufted, rhizomes to 2 cm long; culms to 7.5 dm tall; leaf blades to 12 cm long, 5 mm wide, flat or folded; ligules to 1.5 mm long.

Panicles up to 8 cm long, 2 cm wide; spikelets to 8 mm long, tawny; glumes subequal, to 7 mm long; lowest 2 florets staminate; lemmas moderately hairy, hairs up to 1 mm long, apices deeply bifid, awned; first lemma awn to 6.5 mm long, second to 10.5 mm long, usually geniculate.

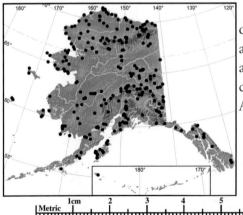

Native grass of well drained and drier alpine and scree areas as well as dry tundra above and north of treeline. The most common sweetgrass species of Alaska.

Alpine sweetgrass
Tribe: Poeae

appressed panicle inflorescence

fertile floret

sterile florets

fertile floret

florets

panicle branch

ligule

florets

spikelets

upper glume

lower glume

Arctic sweetgrass

Anthoxanthum arcticum Veldkamp
Hierochloë pauciflora R. Br.

Perennial, loosely tufted, rhizomatous, rhizomes elongate, to 1 mm thick; linear or spikelike panicle inflorescence; 1-2 spikelets per branch each with 1 perfect and 2 staminate florets, staminate from below and level with the fertile floret on each side, all looking alike; glumes subequal, not inflated and about including all lemmas; staminate florets usually unawned, if awned to 1 mm long.

Plants perennial, loosely tufted or culms solitary, rhizomes elongate, up to 1 mm thick; culms up to 35 cm tall; leaf blades up to 25 cm long, 2 mm in diameter when rolled, involute to convolute; ligules up to 1.3 mm long.

Panicles spikelike, to 4.5 cm long, 0.5 cm wide; spikelets 1 or 2 per branch, to 5 mm long; glumes subequal to 4.7 mm long, shiny; lowest 2 florets staminate; staminate lemmas usually unawned, if awned up to 0.1 mm.

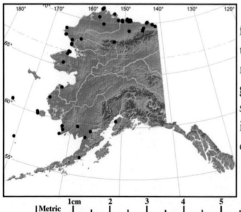

Native grass most often found on coastal wet to saturated tundra areas where it is rooted in mats of moss and organic soils growing over carbonate substrates. Often overlooked as it is often represented by only single culms and small linear panicles.

Arctic sweetgrass
Tribe: Poeae

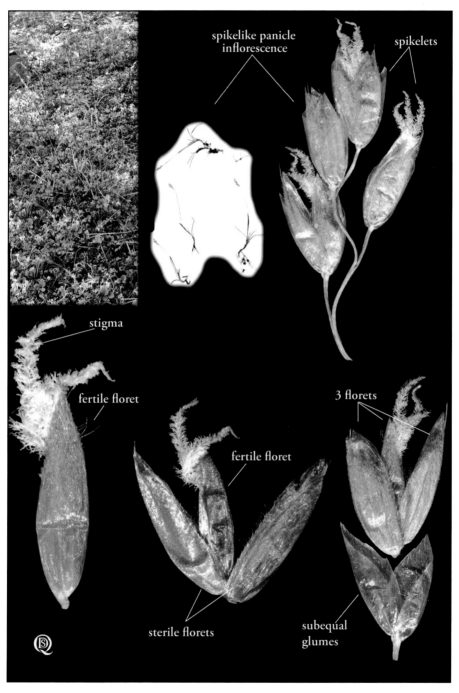

spikelike panicle inflorescence

spikelets

stigma

fertile floret

3 florets

fertile floret

sterile florets

subequal glumes

Hairy sweetgrass

Anthoxanthum hirtum (Schrank) Y. Schouten & Veldkamp
Hierochloë odorata (L.) P. Beauv.

Perennial, loosely tufted, rhizomatous, rhizomes elongate, to 2 mm thick; open pyramidal panicle inflorescence; 3+ spikelets per branch, each with 1 perfect and 2 staminate florets, staminate from below and level with the fertile floret on each side, all looking alike; glumes subequal, not inflated and usually including all lemmas; staminate florets usually unawned, if awned to 1 mm long.

Plants perennial, rhizomatous, rhizomes up to 2 mm thick; culms up to 11 dm tall; flag leaf blades to 6 cm long, 4.5 mm wide, flat; ligules membranous, up to 5.5 mm long.

Inflorescence a pyramidal panicle, to 15 cm long, 10 cm wide, 3+ spikelets per branch; spikelets 3 flowered, broad, tawny, 6 mm long, 2 lower florets staminate, the upper one perfect, glumes subequal, about as long as the included florets; lemmas hairy at the apex, staminate lemmas if awned to 0.1 mm long.

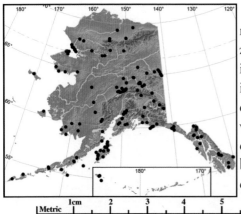

Native grass found in wet meadows, bogs, and moist riparian zones. Culms dispersed, flowering in late summer. Noticed by the inflorescence which often stands out from the surrounding vegetation by shape and glossy color. Has a sweet odor when burned and is distinctly tawny colored.

136

Hairy sweetgrass

Tribe: Poeae

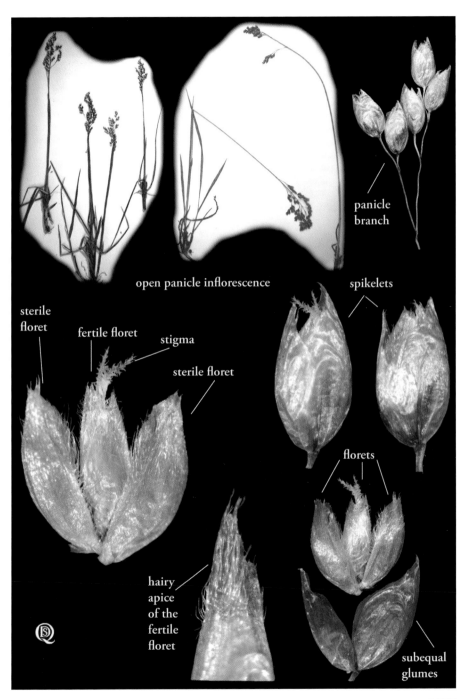

panicle branch

open panicle inflorescence

spikelets

sterile floret

fertile floret

stigma

sterile floret

florets

hairy apice of the fertile floret

subequal glumes

137

Reed canarygrass
Phalaris arundinacea L.

Perennial, rhizomatous, tall grass; inflorescence a long-appressed panicle; ligule membranous; spikelets pedicellate, appearing longer than wide; glumes longer than the florets within them; reduced (sterile) florets present below a single shiny indurate and perfect floret, sterile florets feathery or scalelike structures; florets disarticulate above the glumes at maturity.

Plants perennial, rhizomatous; culms 6-15 dm tall, hollow, smooth, glabrous; vernation rolled; sheaths open, smooth, glabrous; blades 6-16 mm wide, 10-30 cm long, flat, glabrous, sides smooth, edges scaberulous; collars yellow, continuous, constricted; auricles absent; ligules membranous, 2-5 mm long, obtuse, entire, puberulent abaxially.

Inflorescence a long, flattened, crowded, pale panicle, the branches spreading during anthesis; glumes subequal, 4-6 mm long, 3-nerved, rather narrow, acute, flattened, the keel scabrous and very narrowly winged; sterile lemmas 2 feathery structures about 1 mm long or less, very narrow and inconspicuous; fertile lemmas 3-4 mm long, coriaceous and shining, with a few appressed hairs.

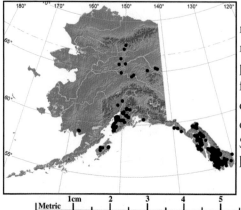

Introduced grass of riparian zones, forest margins, and moist to wet roadsides. Sometimes planted in irrigated meadows for forage. Strongly rhizomatous and once established it may eliminate other native grasses. In areas of Southeast Alaska, reed canarygrass has dominated logged areas.

Reed canarygrass
Tribe: Poeae

spicate
panicle
inflorescence
branch

stigma

stigma

lemma

palea

ligule

glumes

floret

fertile
floret

sterile florets

spikelet

139

Common canarygrass
Phalaris canariensis L.

Annual; spikelike and compressed-panicle inflorescence; ligule membranous; spikelets flattened and about as wide as long; glumes longer than the florets within them; reduced (sterile) florets present below a single shiny indurate and perfect floret, sterile florets feathery or scalelike structures; florets disarticulate above the glumes at maturity.

Plants annual; culms 3-6 dm tall, hollow, smooth, glabrous; vernation rolled; sheaths open, glabrous, scaberulous; blades 4-10 mm wide, 4-20 cm long, flat, glabrous, scaberulous; collars yellow, interrupted, auricles absent; ligules membranous, 3-6 mm long, obtuse, lacerate, glabrous.

Inflorescence an ovate to oblong-ovate, dense and spikelike panicle, 1.5-4 cm long; spikelets flattened, pale, 7-9 mm long, with 2 sterile lemmas; glumes subequal, same length as spikelet, 2-3 mm wide, abruptly pointed, with 3 green nerves, the green keel with a prominent pale wing broadened upward; fertile lemmas acute, appressed-pubescent, 5-6 mm long, obscurely nerved; sterile lemmas feathery or scalelike, about half as long as the fertile one.

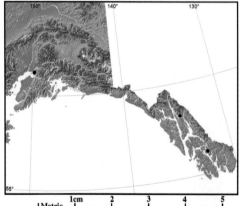

Introduced grass rare in Alaska. May be found in moist disturbed areas around harbors and shipping facilities. Does not appear to persist year to year.

Common canarygrass
Tribe: Poeae

winged keel

winged keel

compressed panicle inflorescence

glumes

spikelets

panicle branches

fertile florets

anthers

palea

ligule

lemma

sterile floret

sterile floret

False oat
Arrhenatherum elatius (L.) P. Beauv. *ex* J. Presl & C. Presl

Perennial, tufted; open-panicle inflorescence; membranous ligule; spikelets pedicellate; glumes 2, not inflated, as long or longer than the lowest floret and often longer than the florets of the spikelet; a single reduced staminate floret similar in appearance to the perfect floret, with a geniculate awn from the back.

Plants perennial, tufted; culms 5-15 dm tall, hollow, smooth, glabrous; vernation rolled; sheaths open, smooth, glabrous; blades 4-10 mm wide, 10-40 cm long, flat, glabrous, scaberulous, or scaberulous on edges only; collars yellow or brownish, continuous, sometimes constricted; auricles absent; ligules membranous, 1-3 mm long, truncate, erose-ciliolate, puberulent abaxially.

Panicle open, sometimes nodding, often shining; spikelets 2-flowered (rarely 3-4), 7-11 mm long, the lower usually staminate, the upper perfect, the rachilla disarticulating above the glumes and protruding beyond the florets, the florets falling together at maturity; glumes rather broad and papery, the first 1-nerved, minutely scabrous, the second a little longer and about as long as the spikelet, 3-nerved; lemmas 8-10 mm long, 7-nerved, hairy on the callus, the lower lemma awned from the back below the middle, the awn 10-14 mm long, twisted, bent, and exserted, the upper lemma awnless, or bristle tipped.

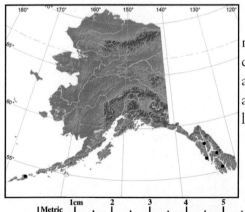

Introduced grass of riparian zones and in very wet cultivated meadows. Noted as an excellent forage grass for large animals. May be used as a landscape grass.

False oat

Tribe: Poeae

panicle inflorescence

spikelets

palea fertile floret

lemma fertile floret

stamen fertile floret

stigma

stamens staminate floret

palea staminate floret

lemma staminate floret

ligule

glumes

2 florets

Velvetgrass, Yorkshire fog

Holcus lanatus L.

Perennial, tufted; appressed to open-panicle inflorescence; membranous ligule; spikelets pedicellate; glumes 2, not inflated, as long or longer than the lowest florets of the spikelet, a single reduced staminate floret, different in appearance to the perfect floret, with a hooked awn; perfect floret awnless.

Plants perennial, tufted, not rhizomatous; culms to 10 dm tall, erect, may be decumbent; sheaths densely pubescent, blades to 20 cm long, 10 mm wide; ligule membranous, to 4 mm long.

Panicles appressed to open, to 20 cm long, to 8 cm wide, branches hairy; spikelets to 6 mm long; glumes longer than the florets, ciliate on the keels and veins, puberulent or villous between the veins, often purple; calluses sparsely hirsute; lemmas to 2.5 mm long, the upper staminate, awned, awn forming a curved hook at maturity.

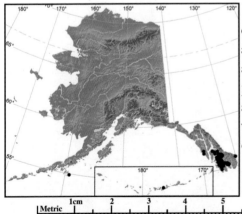

Introduced grass found in disturbed riparian zones, lawns, and meadows. Not abundant in areas where present. Has been a part of the Department of Defense standard seed mixes. In other western states, it is an indicator of overgrazed range or pasture.

144

Velvetgrass, Yorkshire fog

Tribe: Poeae

compressed panicle inflorescence

hairy spikelets

glumes

panicle branch

florets

florets

ligule

Mountain hairgrass
Vahlodea atropurpurea (Wahlenb.) Fr. *ex* Hartm.
Deschampsia atropurpurea var. *latifolia* (Hook.) Scribn. *ex* Macoun

Perennial, tufted; open-panicle inflorescence; ligule membranous; blades firm, flat, folded, or involute; spikelets less than 1 cm long, shiny; glumes exceeding the upper floret; reduced florets absent below 2 perfect florets; lemmas keeled, awned from the middle.

Plants perennial, tufted; culms 1-8 dm tall; leaf blades to 30 cm long, 5 mm wide, flat; ligules membranous, to 4 mm long.

Panicle open, to 20 cm long, branches flexuous, capillary; spikelets less than 1 cm long, distal; glumes 5-6 mm long, longer than the florets; callus hairy; lemmas 2-3 mm long, keeled, obscurely nerved, awned from about the middle; the awn 2.5-3.5 mm long, twisted somewhat near the base, geniculate or straight.

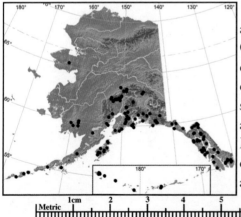

Native grass of alpine and arctic moist to wet riparian areas. Often overlooked because of its delicate inflorescence. Often found on bare ground below melting snow drifts, alpine streambanks, and disturbed bog and pond areas. May be considered a colonizer of deposited sediment and disturbed areas.

Mountain hairgrass

Tribe: Poeae

loose nodding panicle inflorescence

florets

branch

spikelets

anthers

glumes

ligule

Cultivated oats

Avena sativa L.

Annual; ligule membranous; open-panicle inflorescence; spikelets over 1 cm long; glumes longer than the florets within them; 2 or more perfect florets, usually 2 perfect florets, not readily separating; lemmas glabrous, rounded, awned or awnless; when present, awns straight to geniculate.

Plants annual; culms 4-8 dm tall, hollow, smooth, glabrous; vernation rolled; sheaths open, glabrous, smooth or scaberulous; blades 5-10 mm wide, flat, glabrous, smooth or scaberulous; collars yellow, continuous or interrupted, sometimes constricted; auricles absent; ligules membranous, 1.2-2 mm long, truncate or obtuse, erose, glabrous.

Panicles 12-30 cm long, open, fairly erect; spikelets mostly 2-flowered, the rachilla glabrous or only sparsely hirsute, not readily disarticulating; glumes 18-28 mm long; lemmas 14-20 mm long, glabrous, indurate below, 3- to 7-nerved, entire or slightly bifid, callus glabrous or sparsely bearded, awnless or awned, the awns straight to geniculate, 22-35 mm long, attached about the middle.

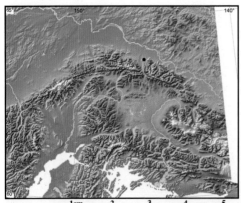

Introduced grass used as an agricultural crop or forage for domestic animals in low-elevation basins. May be used as a cover crop for reclamation of disturbed lands to reduce erosion and promote establishing perennial grasses and shrubs. Occasionally escaped from croplands, but not persistent.

Cultivated oats

Tribe: Poeae

spikelet with awnless lemmas

open panicle inflorescence

panicle spikelets

florets with awnless lemmas

spikelet with awned lemmas

ligule

florets with awned lemmas

Wild oats
Avena fatua L.

Annual; ligule membranous; open-panicle inflorescence; spikelets over 1 cm long; glumes longer than the florets within them; 2 or more perfect florets, usually 3, readily separating and awned from the middle of the lemmas, lemmas clothed with stiff brown hairs (hairs sometimes white or scant); awns stout, geniculate, twisted.

Plants annual; culms 4.8-9 dm tall, hollow, smooth, glabrous; vernation rolled; sheaths open, smooth, glabrous; blades 3-10 mm wide, flat, glabrous, scaberulous to scabrous, edges occasionally ciliolate below; collars glabrous or sparsely pilose; auricles absent; ligules membranous, 3-4.2 mm long, acute, erose, glabrous, or puberulent abaxially.

Panicles 10-25 cm long, somewhat nodding; spikelets mostly 3-flowered, the rachilla densely bearded, readily disarticulating; glumes 19-28 mm long, acuminate; lemmas 14-20 mm long, clothed with stiff brown hairs, these sometimes white or sparse, indurate below, 5- to 7-nerved, bifid, the callus densely bearded, awned, the awn twisted and geniculate, 28-45 mm long, attached above the middle.

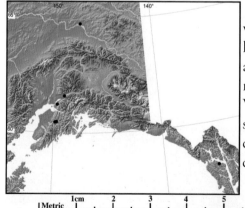

Introduced grass associated with agricultural crops of low-elevation basins, disturbed areas, and along roadsides. Does not appear to persist in Alaska. When present, it is considered a serious agricultural pest contaminating livestock feed and commercial seed sources.

Wild oats

Tribe: Poeae

open panicle
inflorescence

bifid
lemma

2 - 3 fertile
florets

bifid lemmas

stout
geniculate
twisted
awns

stiff brown
hairy lemmas

lower
glume

upper
glume

Perennial ryegrass; Perennial darnel
Lolium perenne L.

Perennial, long-lived, tufted; ligule membranous; spike inflorescence; spikelets placed edgewise to the rachis; lower glume missing except in the uppermost spikelet, the upper glume of the lower spikelets shorter than the multiple fertile florets within it; lemma nerves converging toward the tip, not prominent, unawned or sometimes awned.

Plants perennial, tufted; culms hollow, smooth, glabrous; vernation rolled; sheaths open, smooth, glabrous; blades involute, smooth, glabrous; collars yellow or purple, continuous; auricles 0.5-0.7 mm long; ligules membranous, about 1.1 mm long, obtuse, entire, glabrous.

Spikes erect, narrow, 8-11 cm long; spikelets 2-22 mm long, 2-10 florets; the single glume to 15 mm long, nearly as long as the spikelet, 7-9 nerved; lemmas to 9 mm long, awned or sometimes awned, awns when present to 8 mm long.

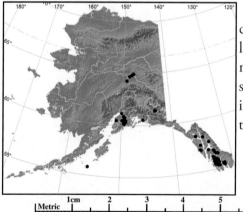

Introduced grass. Used as cover crops, roadside reclamations, lawns, and can escape to occupy nearby disturbed areas. Often substituted for annual ryegrass in seed mixes when fast growing temporary cover is required.

Perennial ryegrass; Perennial darnel

Tribe: Poeae

spike
inflorescence

ligule

florets

lemma

palea

glume

rachis

spikelet
edgewise
to the rachis

spikelets

rachis

glume

lemma

glume

glume

lemma

153

Italian ryegrass; Italian darnel
Lolium multiflorum Lam.

Annual or short-lived tufted perennial; ligule membranous; spike inflorescence; spikelets placed edgewise to the rachis, lower glume missing except in the uppermost spikelet, the upper glume of the lower spikelets shorter than the multiple fertile florets within it; lemma nerves converging toward the tip, not prominent, awned, rarely unawned.

Plants annual or short-lived perennials, tufted; culms hollow, smooth, glabrous; vernation rolled; sheaths open, smooth, glabrous; blades flat, glabrous, smooth or edges scabrous; collars yellow or brown, continuous or interrupted, sometimes constricted; auricles 0.7-1.3 mm long; ligules membranous, 0.9-1 mm long, truncate, ciliolate, glabrous.

Spikes erect, narrow, 9-18 cm long; spikelets 10-15 mm long, 10-22 florets; the single glume to 18 mm long, about half as long as the spikelet, to 28 mm long, 7-nerved; lemmas to 8.5 mm long, 5-nerved; at least the upper florets awned, to 15 mm long from a minutely bifid apex.

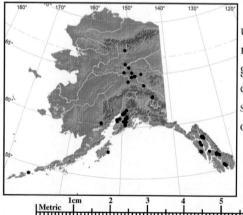

Introduced grass often used as temporary cover or as a nurse crop to protect the slower growing perennial grasses. May escape from where reclamation seed mixes have been planted and occupy other disturbed areas.

154

Italian ryegrass; Italian darnel
Tribe: Poeae

spike inflorescence

spikelets placed edgewise on rachis

spike inflorescence

florets

paleas

glume

rachis

palea

lemma

lemmas

floret

palea

rachillas

ligule

glume

glume

lemma

lemma

Slender hairgrass
Deschampsia elongata (Hook.) Munro

Perennial, tufted; appressed-panicle inflorescence more than one-fourth the length of the culm; ligule membranous; blades firm, flat, folded, or involute; spikelets less than 1 cm long, shiny; upper lemma exceeding the lower glume, usually all lemmas included within the upper glume; reduced florets absent below 2 perfect florets; lemmas awned from the middle of the lemmas, about twice as long as florets.

Plants perennial, tufted; culms 3-12 dm tall, hollow, smooth, glabrous; vernation folded; sheaths open, smooth, glabrous; blades 1-1.5 mm wide, involute, glabrous, scabrous and coarsely veined adaxially, smooth abaxially, edges scabrous; collars indistinct; auricles absent; ligules membranous, 1-2.5 mm long, acute, entire, glabrous.

Panicle narrow, as much as 30 cm long, the capillary branches appressed; spikelets on short-appressed pedicels; glumes to 6 mm long, 3-nerved, equaling or slightly exceeding the florets; lemmas to 4.3 mm long, with a slender awn from below the middle, the awn to 6 mm long, the callus hairs about half as long as the lemma.

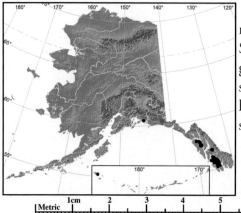

Native grass common to mountain riparian zones in Southeastern Alaska. A late seral grass often found on edges of streambanks, small ponds, willow hummocks, and in meadows near spruce/hemlock forest margins.

Slender hairgrass

Tribe: Poeae

appressed panicle
spikelets

florets

glumes

awned florets

palea

stigma

lemma

ligule

glumes

florets

spikelet

Narrow panicle hairgrass
Deschampsia brevifolia R. Br.

Perennial, tufted; contracted to somewhat open inflorescence; ligule membranous; blades firm, flat, folded, or involute; spikelets overlapping each other and often clustered near the end of branches, less than 1 cm long, shiny; upper lemma exceeding the lower glume, usually all lemmas included within the upper glume; glumes mostly purple; reduced florets absent below 2 perfect florets; lemmas awned from the middle, less than twice as long as the florets.

Plants perennial, tufted; culms to 55 cm tall, erect; leaves forming a basal tuft, blades to 16 cm long, 2 mm wide when flat, folded to involute; ligules membranous to 4.5 mm long.

Panicles to 12 cm long, 0.5-2 (11) cm wide, wider at anthesis; branches to 6 cm long, straight, erect to ascending, spikelet bearing to the base; 2-3 overlapping florets often clustered near the ends of branches; lemmas included within the upper glume; callus hairs to 2 mm long; awns to 4 mm long, usually as long or longer than the lemma, straight or slightly geniculate.

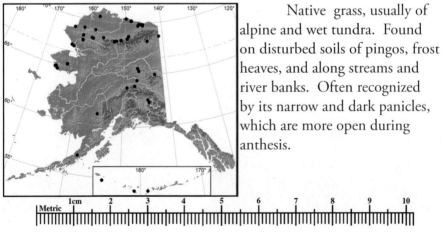

Native grass, usually of alpine and wet tundra. Found on disturbed soils of pingos, frost heaves, and along streams and river banks. Often recognized by its narrow and dark panicles, which are more open during anthesis.

Narrow panicle hairgrass
Tribe: Poeae

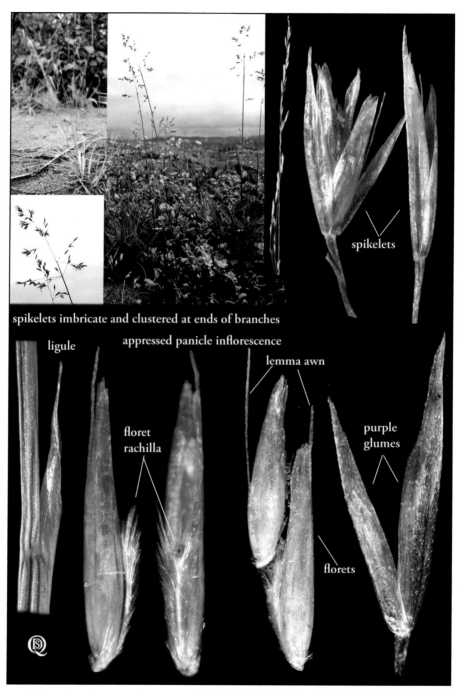

spikelets

spikelets imbricate and clustered at ends of branches

ligule

appressed panicle inflorescence

lemma awn

floret
rachilla

purple
glumes

florets

Deschampsie naine

Deschampsia sukatschewii (Popl.) Roshev.

D. caespitosa (L.) Beauv. subsp. *orientalis* Hultén

Perennial, densely tufted, tuft up to 20 cm in diameter, culms generally to 7 dm tall; open and pyramidal panicle-inflorescence; ligule membranous; leaves basal, rolled, rarely flat, somewhat capillary, involute, new leaves less than 0.5 mm wide; spikelets less than 1 cm long, shiny, not overlapping each other along and at the end of branches; upper lemma exceeding the lower glume, usually all lemmas included within the upper glume; lower glume smooth over the midvein; reduced florets absent below 2 perfect florets; lemmas awned from the middle of the lemmas, less than twice as long as the florets.

Plants perennial, densely tufted; culms 5 cm up to 7 dm tall, in the arctic generally much shorter, erect, often strongly geniculate at the first node; leaves mostly basal forming a dense tuft 5-20 cm in diameter, blades up to 8 cm long, rolled and involute; ligules up to 8 mm long.

Panicles open and pyramidal, sometimes ovate to closed, up to 17 cm long, 9 cm wide, branches spreading, reflexed, flexuous; spikelets up to 5.2 mm long, shiny; glumes acute to acuminate, upper generally exceeding the lowest floret; callus hairs up to 1 mm long; lemmas up to 4 mm long, awned, from at or below the middle, straight, slender, slightly or not exserted.

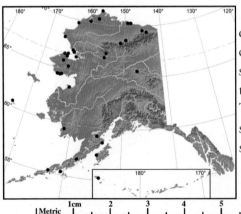

Native grass forming dense tufts along the Alaska arctic coast. Recognized by being rather short, with fine involute leaves that form a dense tuft. The panicle is generally open, somewhat capillary, and spread out.

Deschampsie naine

Tribe: Poeae

spikelets not usually imbricate

panicle branch

ligule

open panicle inflorescence

3 to 5 nerve lower leaf blade

florets

florets

spikelet and glumes

spikelet and glumes

Beringian hairgrass

Deschampsia cespitosa subsp. *beringensis* (Hultén) W.E. Lawr.

Perennial, somewhat loosely tufted, often glaucous, culms to 14 dm tall; open-panicle inflorescence; ligule membranous; leaves mostly basal, usually some flat, others rolled or involute, at least some new leaves 2-4 mm wide; spikelets less than 1 cm long, shiny, not overlapping each other along and at the end of branches; glumes lanceolate, to 7.5 mm long; upper lemma exceeds the lower glume, usually all lemmas included within the upper glume, lower glume scabridulous distally over the midvein; reduced florets absent below 2 perfect florets; lemmas awned from the lower third of the lemmas, awns conspicuously exceeding the lemmas.

Plants perennial, tufted; culms up to 14 dm tall, erect, not rooting at the lower nodes; leaves mostly basal, sometimes forming a dense tuft; blades up to 12 cm long, 4 mm wide, some flat, others involute; ligules membranous up to 13 mm long.

Panicle to 40 cm long, 30 cm wide, open, and nodding; spikelets to 8 mm long, shiny, not overlapping each other along and at the end of branches; glumes narrow, lower glume scabridulous distally over the midvein; upper lemma exceeding the lower glume, usually included within the upper glume; reduced florets absent below 2 perfect florets; lemmas awned, awn to 8 mm long, exceeding the lemmas.

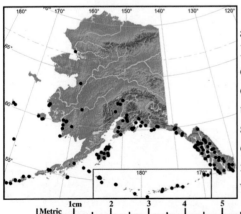

Native grass common along the coastal areas of Alaska. Found in a wide variety of soil conditions, but most often occurs on silts and gravels. Very tall, glaucous, with long narrow spikelets and glumes. Alaska's cultivar 'Norcoast' is widely used for revegetation of disturbed areas within its natural range.

162

open panicle inflorescence

ligule

panicle branch

rachilla

awns longer than lemmas

florets

florets

upper glume

lower glume

lemma

stigma

palea

spikelets

Tufted hairgrass
Deschampsia cespitosa (L.) P. Beauv. subsp. *cespitosa*

Perennial, tufted, not glaucous, culms 15 dm tall; open-panicle inflorescence; ligule membranous; leaves mostly basal, usually some flat, at least some new leaves 1-4 mm wide; spikelets less than 1 cm long, shiny, not overlapping each other along and at the end of branches; glumes broader in comparison to length, to 6 mm long; upper lemma exceeding the lower glume, usually all lemmas included within the upper glume, lower glume scabridulous distally over the midvein; reduced florets absent below 2 perfect florets; lemmas awned from the lower third of the lemmas, awns do not or just exceed the lemma.

Plants perennial, tufted; culms to 15 dm tall, erect, not rooting at the lower nodes; leaves mostly basal, sometimes forming a dense tuft; blades to 30 cm long, to 4 mm wide, some flat the others involute; ligules membranous to 13 mm long.

Panicle to 30 cm long, to 30 cm wide, open, loose and nodding; spikelets to 7 mm long, shiny, not usually imbricate along and at the end of branches; glumes subequal, acute, to 6 mm long, lower glume scabridulous distally over the mid-vein; upper lemma exceeding the lower glume, usually all lemmas included within the upper glume; reduced florets absent below 2 perfect florets; lemmas awned from near base, the awn to 8 mm long, exceeded by or exceeding the distal floret.

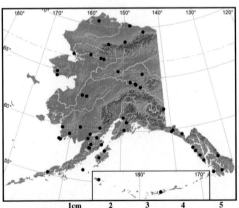

Native grass common across Alaska except at very high elevations. Often found on deposited sediment of streams and rivers. Recognized by being very tufted and having an open, nodding, and shiny panicle inflorescence. Alaska's cultivar 'Nortran' has been widely used for revegetation of disturbed areas.

Tufted hairgrass
Tribe: Aveneae
Sub-Tribe: Avenineae

branch and spikelets

florets

palea

rudiment floret

lemma

awned lemma

spikelets

palea

awned lemma

stigma

glumes

ligule

165

Siberian trisetum
Trisetum sibiricum Rupr.

Perennial, rhizomatous; broadly spicate-panicle inflorescence; ligule membranous; blades firm, flat, folded, or involute; spikelets less than 1 cm long, in fascicles; upper lemma exceeding the lower glume, usually all lemmas included within the upper glume, reduced florets absent below 2 perfect florets; lemmas awned and strongly geniculate.

Plants perennial, rhizomatous; culms to 6.5 dm tall, solitary, decumbent; blades to 24 cm long, 7 mm wide, flat, erect or ascending; ligules membranous, to 3.5 mm long.

Panicle inflorescence, ovate-spicate sometimes interrupted, shiny, to 16 cm long, 6 cm wide, branches appressed-ascending, spikelets distal; spikelets to 8 mm long, usually 2 fertile florets; glumes lanceolate, lower glumes to 4.5 mm long, upper to 8 mm long; lemmas to 7 mm long, awned, awns to 10+ mm long, from the upper third, exceeding the lemma apices, flexuous, bent, and twisted.

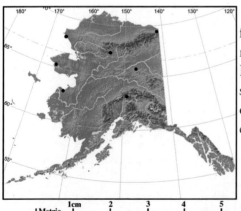

Native riparian grass found on streambanks, moist meadows, and coastal beaches. Highly rhizomatous and the single culms of plants are easily overlooked. Not a commonly encountered species in Alaska.

Siberian trisetum

Tribe: Poeae

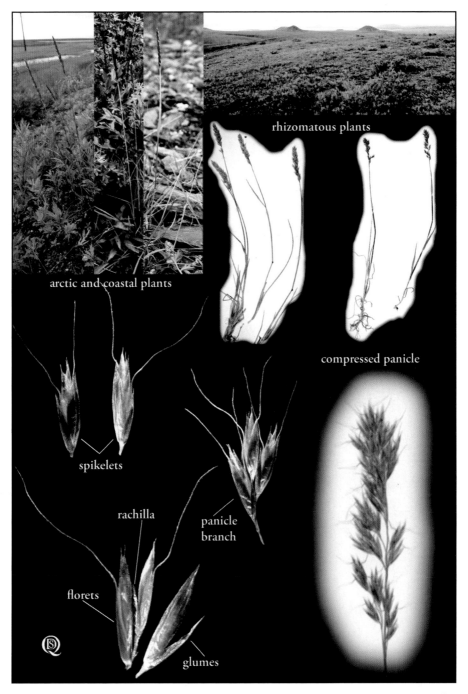

rhizomatous plants

arctic and coastal plants

compressed panicle

spikelets

rachilla

panicle branch

florets

glumes

Spike trisetum

Trisetum spicatum (L.) K. Richt.
Trisetum spicatum (L.) Richter subsp. a*laskanum* (Nash) Hultén
Trisetum spicatum subsp. *molle* (Michx.) Hultén

Perennial, tufted, not rhizomatous; dense spicate-panicle inflorescence; ligule membranous; blades firm, flat, folded, or involute; spikelets to 7.5 mm long, in fascicles; glumes subequal; upper lemma exceeding the lower glume, usually all lemmas included within the upper glume, reduced florets absent below 2 perfect florets; lemmas awned and strongly geniculate.

Plants perennial, tufted; culms to 12 dm tall, nodes puberulent; sheaths open, smooth, glabrous to densely pilose; blades mostly to 20 cm long, 1-5 mm wide; ligules membranous, 1.1-1.3 mm long.

Panicle mostly to 30 cm long, 1-2.5 cm wide, mostly spicate, often interrupted at the base; spikelets to 7.5 mm long, sessile, subsessile or on short pedicels, in fascicles on short branches, usually 2 fertile florets; first glume 5-7 mm long, 1-nerved, rather narrow, second glume 6-8 mm long, wider, 3- to 5-nerved, both glumes smooth or scabrous on the keel; lemmas 5 mm long, the awn 4-6 mm long, geniculate, flexuous at base, attached above the middle.

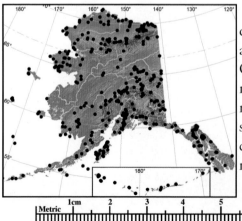

Native grass widely distributed throughout Alaska and very common worldwide. Occurs on drier areas of mountain meadows, roadsides, forest margins, dry tundra and subalpine to alpine slopes. Being commercialized for use in revegetation and erosion control.

spicate
panicle
inflorescence

spikelets

dorsal
lemma
awn

2 florets

ligule

glumes

spikelet

Nodding trisetum

Trisetum cernuum Trin.

Perennial, tufted, not rhizomatous; appressed to open and often drooping-panicle inflorescence; ligule membranous; blades, flat, lax; spikelet-bearing near branch apices, spikelets to 1.2 cm long; glumes unequal, upper glume shorter than the lowest florets, usually 2 perfect florets below 1-2 reduced florets; lemmas awned, awns straight to somewhat geniculate.

Plants perennial, tufted, not rhizomatous; culms to 11 dm tall, erect; leaves to 20+ cm long, 12 mm wide, 2-3 per culm, flat, lax at maturity; ligule membranous to 3 mm long.

Panicles up to 30 cm long, 9 cm wide, open, nodding, branches to 12 cm long, spikelet-bearing near the apices, lower half bare; spikelets to 1.2 cm long, usually 2 perfect florets below 1-2 reduced florets; glumes unequal, the longer upper glume shorter than the lowest florets, 2-3 times as wide as the lower glume; lemmas awned, awns to 14 mm long, from above the middle to just below bifid tip, exceeding the lemma apices, flexuous.

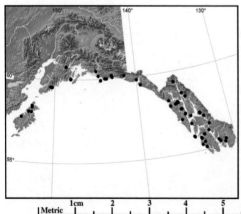

Native grass common to open coastal spruce and hemlock forests and forest margins. Occupies moist woods, streambanks, lakeshores, ponds, floodplains, and coastlines.

170

nodding panicle inflorescence

lemma awns

spikelet bearing near tip of branches

spikelets

panicle branches

rachilla

2 florets of spikelet

unequal glumes

ligule

Slender wedgegrass
Sphenopholis intermedia (Rydb.) Rydb.

Perennial, tufted; somewhat open spicate-panicle inflorescence, often nodding; membranous ligule; leaf blades lax; glumes not exceeding, but about equal to or just shorter than the multiple perfect florets within them, longer than the lowest floret, lower glume less than 1/3 as wide as the upper; florets disarticulate below the glumes; lemmas awnless or short, less than 2 mm long.

Plants perennial, tufted; culms 3-10 dm tall; blades 2-6 mm wide, 8-15 cm long, flat, lax, scaberulous to sparsely pilose; sheaths glabrous to pubescent; ligules 1-3 mm long.

Panicle 8-20 cm long, from rather dense to open, nodding, branches spikelet-bearing to the base; spikelets 2.5-4 mm long, 2 to 3 florets, lower glume 1.5-2 mm long or sometimes longer, narrow, less than 1/3 as wide as the upper glume; upper glume 1.3-3.3 mm long, 4-5 times broader than the first, oblanceolate to obovate, both glumes scabrous on keel; lemmas 2.3-3 mm long, obscurely nerved, somewhat narrower than the second glume, unawned or subacute, rarely mucronate.

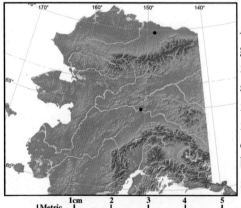

Native grass. Rare in Alaska. Most often described as growing along meadows or damp rocky woods, especially along slowly trickling streams. In riparian zones, it appears to be restricted to clay soils that dry out during the growing season. May be mistaken for *Koeleria macrantha.*

Slender wedgegrass

Tribe: Poeae

inflorescence

appressed to open panicle inflorescence

panicle branch

spikelets

wedge shape upper glume

2 fertile florets

fertile florets

lower glume less than 1/3 as wide as upper glume

ligule

paleas

rachilla

lemmas

rachilla

Eurasian Junegrass

Koeleria asiatica Domin

Perennial, loosely tufted, shortly rhizomatous; spicate-panicle inflorescence; culms pubescent; ligule membranous; sheaths open; blades basal, narrow, involute, boat-tipped; spikelets less than 1 cm long; upper lemma exceeding the lower glume, usually all lemmas included within the upper glume, reduced florets absent below 2 perfect florets, disarticulation above the glumes; lemmas pubescent, awnless, sometimes short awned.

Plants perennial, tufted, rhizomes short; culms to 3.5 dm tall, pubescent throughout; leaf blades to 20 cm long, to 3 mm wide, involute, stiff; ligules to 2.5 mm long.

Panicles spicate, somewhat interrupted at the base, branches villous; spikelets to 6.5 mm long, mostly 2 florets; lemmas just longer than the glumes, pubescent, awned tipped to about 1.4 mm long.

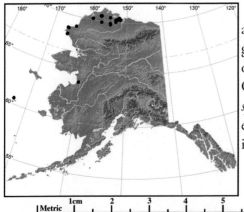

Native grass found on dry areas of dry tundra, creek beds, gravel bars, and rocky slopes most often in northwestern Alaska. Often mistaken for *Trisetum spicatum* in the field, but on close examination awns are inconspicuous.

174

Eurasian Junegrass

Tribe: Poeae

compressed panicle inflorescence

upper sand banks/dunes of Meade River

boat tipped leaf blade

palea

florets

panicle

lemma

hairy sheath

anthers

lemma
palea

spikelets

ligule

glumes

175

Fisher's tundragrass
Dupontia fisheri R. Br. subsp. *fisheri*
Dupontia fisheri R. Br.

Perennial, rhizomatous; open-panicle inflorescence, branches mostly erect; less than 30 cm tall; ligule membranous; sheaths closed over 1/2 their length; leaves not boat tipped, 2-6 mm wide; spikelets less than 1 cm long; glumes subequal to just longer than the spikelets, blunt; reduced florets absent below 2 perfect florets, disarticulation above the glumes, upper lemma exceeding the lower glume, usually all lemmas included within the upper glume, awnless, apices obtuse, pubescent.

Plants perennial, rhizomatous, culms less than 30 cm tall, erect, glabrous; sheaths closed over 1/2 their length; leaf blades up to 13 cm long, 3 mm wide; ligules to 5.5 mm long.

Panicles to 18 cm long, 6 cm wide, branches mostly erect; spikelets to 9 mm long; glumes subequal, equaling or usually exceeding the distal florets, unawned; reduced florets absent below 2 perfect florets, disarticulation above the glumes; lemmas awnless, apices obtuse, pubescent.

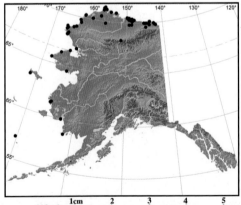

Native grass common to wet meadows, wet tundra, marshes and along streams, lakeshores and ponds where new sediment is deposited. This subspecies grows along the coast and further inland than *D. fisheri* subsp. *psilosantha*.

176

Fisher's tundragrass

Tribe: Poeae

panicle inflorescence

panicle branch

spikelets

floret and glumes
extended midvein
of lemma
glabrous
florets

hairy
florets

short
callus hairs

ligule

Fisher's tundragrass
Dupontia fisheri R. Br. subsp. *psilosantha* (Rupr.) Hultén
Dupontia fisheri R. Br.

Perennial, rhizomatous; open-panicle inflorescence, branches mostly erect; over 30 cm tall; ligule membranous; sheaths closed over ½ their length; leaves not boat tipped, 2-6 mm wide; spikelets less than 1 cm long; glumes subequal to just longer than the spikelets, long-acuminate; reduced florets absent below 2 perfect florets, disarticulation above the glumes, upper lemma exceeding the lower glume, usually all lemmas included within the upper glume, awnless, apices acute, mostly glabrous, awnless, apices acute to acuminate, glabrous.

Plants perennial, rhizomatous, culms usually over 30 cm tall, glabrous; sheaths closed over 1/2 their length; leaf blades to 13 cm long, 3 mm wide; ligules up to 5.5 mm long.

Panicles to 18 cm long, 6 cm wide, branches mostly erect; spikelets to 9 mm long; glumes subequal to just longer than the spikelets, long-acuminate unawned; reduced florets absent below 2 perfect florets, disarticulation above the glumes; lemma exceeding the lower glume, usually all lemmas included within the upper glume, awnless, apices, mostly glabrous, acute to acuminate.

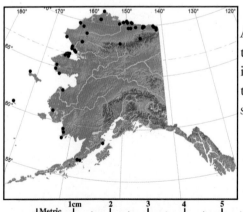

Native grass common to Alaska's coastal marshes and wet tundra. Not found on inland sites. Occupies wet tundra, marshes, and along streams, lakeshores, and ponds.

178

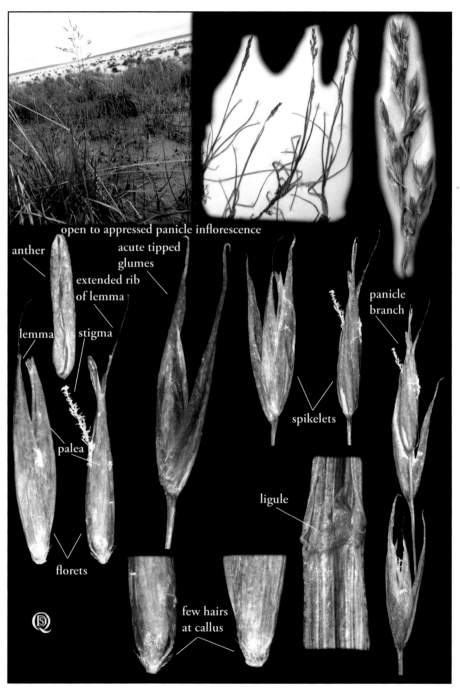

open to appressed panicle inflorescence

anther

acute tipped glumes

extended rib of lemma

lemma

stigma

panicle branch

palea

spikelets

florets

ligule

few hairs at callus

Labrador bluegrass

×*Duarctopoa labradorica* (Steud.) R. J. Soreng & L.J. Gillespie
×*Dupoa labradorica* (Steudel.) J. Cay. & Darbysh.

Perennial, rhizomatous, dense to open-panicle inflorescence; over 30 cm tall: ligule membranous; sheaths closed ⅓-⅔ their length; leaves not boat-tipped, 2-6 mm wide; spikelets less than 1 cm long, 2-4 sterile florets; lower glume shorter to subequal to the lower lemma, upper glume subequal to just shorter to the upper lemma; anthers 3, indehiscent; floret disarticulation above the glumes; lemmas awnless.

Plants perennial; rhizomatous, rhizomes to 1.5 mm thick; culms to 8 dm tall, glabrous, often glaucous, several nodes; ligules membranous; sheaths closed for ⅓-⅔ their length, seldom glaucous; auricles absent; blades glabrous, to 20 cm long, to 6 mm wide.

Panicles to 20 cm long, open to dense; branches glabrous, spikelet-bearing to the base; spikelets to 10 mm long; 2-4 sterile florets; lower glume subequal to shorter to the lower lemma, upper glume subequal to just shorter to the upper lemma; floret disarticulation above the glumes, lemmas awnless; 3 indehiscent anthers.

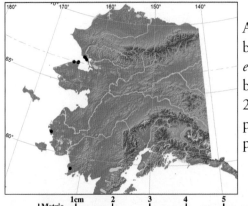

Native grass of the Arctic coast. A sterile hybrid between *Dupontia fisheri* and *Poa eminens*. Distribution is unclear, but it must be confined to the 2 parent species (*Poa eminens* p. 230 and *Dupontia fisheri* p. 176).

Labrador bluegrass

Tribe: Poeae

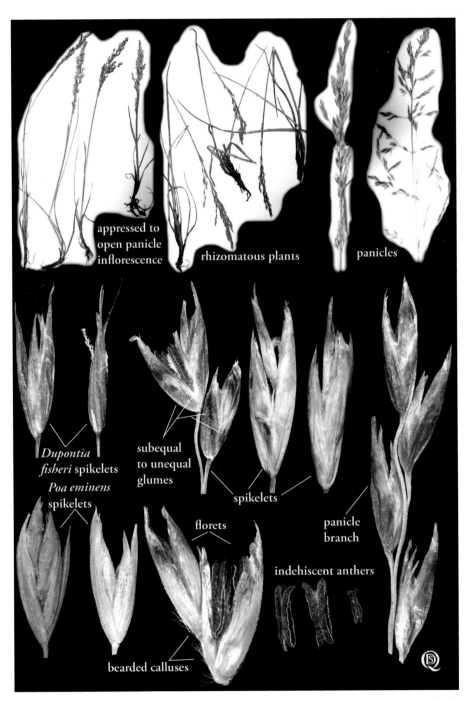

appressed to open panicle inflorescence

rhizomatous plants

panicles

Dupontia fisheri spikelets

Poa eminens spikelets

subequal to unequal glumes

spikelets

florets

panicle branch

indehiscent anthers

bearded calluses

181

Orchardgrass
Dactylis glomerata L.

Perennial, tufted; panicle inflorescence; spikelets laterally compressed, relatively small, several flowered, glumes 2, glumes shorter than the lowest floret, ligule membranous; lemma nerves converging toward the tip; spikelets crowded in 1-sided clusters at the end of naked panicle branches.

Plants perennial, tufted; culms 3-12 dm tall, hollow, smooth, glabrous; vernation folded; sheaths closed, glabrous, scaberulous to scabrous; blades 2-8 mm wide, flat or folded, glabrous, scabrous; collars yellow, continuous, sometimes constricted; auricles absent; ligules membranous, 2-3 mm long, truncate, ciliolate, glabrous.

Panicle 5-20 cm long, first internode long, main branches long, additional branches short, lower branches naked below; spikelets 5-8 mm long, 2- to 5-flowered in dense clusters on 1 side of the rachis branch; glumes 3-6 mm long, 1-nerved, glabrous or pubescent, awn tipped; lemmas 4-6.5 mm long, 5-nerved with a short awn from the tip.

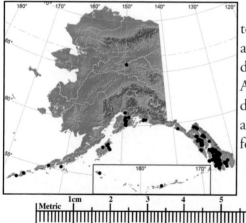

Introduced grass common to irrigated, improved pastures and hayfields, as well as irrigation ditches in the lower 48 states. In Alaska, usually associated with disturbed habitats and agricultural areas where it has been tried as a forage grass.

Orchardgrass

Tribe: Poeae

crowded clusters of spikelets at end of branches

ligule

florets

florets

spikelets

lemma

glumes

Tall fescue

Schedonorus arundinaceus (Schreb.) Dumort.

Festuca arundinacea Schreb.

Perennial, tufted with short rhizomes; panicle inflorescence, erect, open, often nodding; ligule membranous; auricles present and ciliate; spikelets with many florets, relatively small, laterally compressed, evenly distributed on inflorescence branches; leaves not boat tipped shaped, blades flat, over 3 mm wide; glumes usually shorter than the lowest floret; lemmas to 11.5 mm long, nerves converging towards the tip, awnless or awned, if awned awns 1-4 mm long from the tip.

Plants perennial, tufted sometimes rhizomatous; culms to 20 dm tall, hollow, smooth, glabrous, erect or geniculate; vernation rolled; sheaths open, smooth, glabrous; blades to 30 cm long, to 12 mm wide, flat or involute, glabrous, smooth or scabrous adaxially, smooth abaxially, edges scabrous; collars yellow, continuous or interrupted, sometimes constricted; auricles 0.5-0.7 mm long, ciliate; ligules membranous, to 2 mm long, truncate, entire, glabrous.

Panicle erect, open 10-35 cm long; spikelets 10-15 mm long, 3-9 florets; glumes roughly equal, lower 3-6 mm long, 1-nerved, upper 4.5-7 mm long, 3-nerved; lemmas to 11.5 mm long, 5-nerved, awnless or with a fine rough awn to 4 mm long; palea equal to lemma.

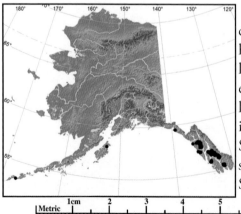

Introduced riparian grass common to irrigated pastures, hayfields, irrigation ditches, lawns, roadsides, and low elevation moist meadows of the lower western states. In Alaska, its historic use has been on Forest Service lands for logging and road seedings. Now widespread in Southeast Alaska.

Tall fescue
Tribe: Poeae

ligule

auricles often ciliate

lemma

palea

rachilla

florets

glumes

spikelet

Meadow fescue

Schedonorus pratensis (Huds.) P. Beauv.

Festuca pratensis Huds.; *Festuca elatior* L.

Perennial, tufted, sometimes rhizomatous; erect, panicle inflorescence, generally narrow; ligule membranous; auricles present, glabrous; spikelets many florets, relatively small, laterally compressed, evenly distributed on inflorescence branches; leaf blades flat, usually over 3 mm wide; glumes usually shorter than the lowest floret; lemmas usually less than 8 mm long, nerves converging towards the tip, awnless or awned, if awned 0.2 mm long.

Plants perennial, tufted, sometimes rhizomatous; culms to 13 dm tall, hollow, smooth, glabrous; vernation rolled; sheaths open, smooth, glabrous; blades to 7 mm wide, 10-25 cm long, flat, smooth, glabrous; collars indistinct, or yellow, continuous; auricles 0.4-1.7 mm long, glabrous; ligules membranous, 0.3-0.5 mm long, truncate, entire, glabrous.

Panicle mostly erect, 10-25 cm long, contracted after flowering, spikelet-bearing nearly to base; spikelets to 17 mm long, to 12 florets; glumes to 5 mm long, lanceolate; lemmas oblong-lanceolate, to 8 mm long, smooth, coriaceous, apex acute, awnless or rarely short awned, if awned to 0.2 mm long.

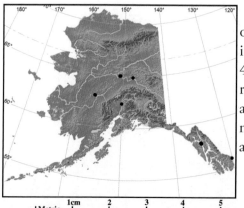

Introduced riparian grass often grown in improved and irrigated pastures of the lower 48 states. Sporadic, found along roadsides, hillslopes, and disturbed areas with sufficient soil moisture near present or past agricultural areas.

186

Meadow fescue
Tribe: Poeae

open panicle spikelets

lemma

floret

palea

glumes

spikelet

ligule

auricles
glabrous

Bearded fescue

Festuca subulata Trin.

Perennial, loosely tufted, without rhizomes; open drooping panicle inflorescence; ligule membranous; auricles absent; leaves not boat tipped, blades mostly flat, 3-10 mm wide; spikelets not in 1-sided clusters, several flowered, relatively small, laterally compressed, drooping from the end of naked branches; spikelet glumes shorter than the included florets, narrow and acuminate; lemma nerves converge at the scaberulous apex, awns usually 5-15 mm long.

Plants perennial, tufted; culms 5-10 dm tall; leaf blades 3-10 mm wide, usually flat, not boat-tipped; auricles absent; ligules membranous.

Panicle loose, open, drooping, 15-40 cm long, the branches mostly in 2's and 3's, naked below, finally spreading or reflexed, the lower as much as 15 cm long; spikelets loosely 3 to 5 florets; glumes narrow, acuminate, the first about 3 mm, the second about 5 mm long; lemmas somewhat keeled, scaberulous toward the apex, the intermediate nerves obscure, the tip attenuate into an awn 5-15 mm long.

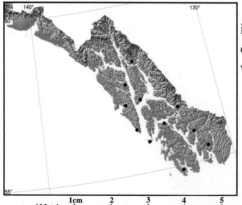

Native grass relatively rare in Alaska and confined to shady, cool, streambanks and moist woody thickets.

Bearded fescue

Tribe: Poeae

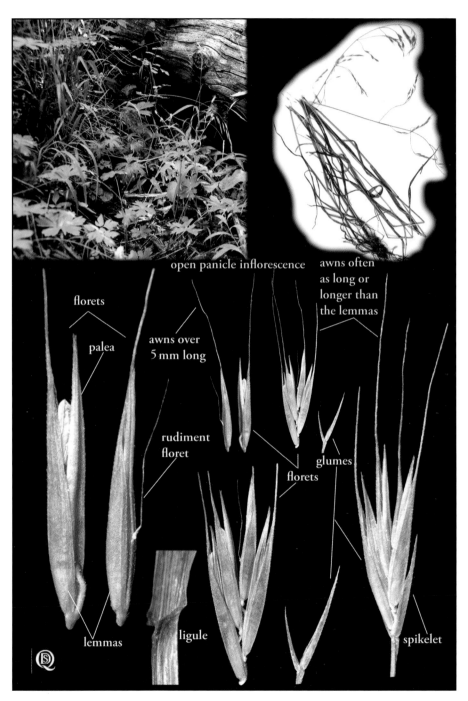

florets

palea

awns over
5 mm long

open panicle inflorescence

awns often
as long or
longer than
the lemmas

rudiment
floret

glumes

florets

lemmas

ligule

spikelet

Arctic red fescue
Festuca rubra subsp. *arctica* (Hack.) Govor.

Perennial, rhizomatous; narrow-panicle inflorescence, exserted above the uppermost sheath; leaves not boat tipped, blades involute and if flat, less than 3 mm wide; membranous ligule; auricles absent; spikelets not in 1-sided clusters, several flowered, relatively small, laterally compressed to somewhat rounded on the back; spikelet glumes shorter than the multiple fertile florets within them; lemma nerves converging at the summit, lemmas mostly pilose, awns usually 0.5-1.6 mm long.

Plants perennial, rhizomatous, loosely to densely tufted; culms to 6 dm tall; mature inflorescence well exserted from uppermost sheath; cauline leaf blades mostly folded, less than 3 mm wide, not boat tipped; flag leaf blades 2-6 cm long; ligules membranous.

Narrow-panicle inflorescence, to 7 cm long, sparsely branched; branches usually stiff, erect, scabrous or pubescent; spikelets to 13 mm long, to 7 florets; glumes acute to acuminate, often pilose near the apices; lemmas to 6.5 mm long usually densely to moderately pilose; awns usually 0.5-1.6 mm long; anthers usually 2.5-3 mm long.

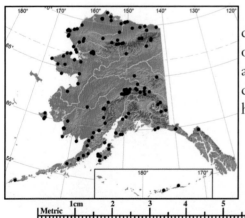

Native grass common to dry tundra, gravel bars, glacial outwashes, streambanks, beaches, and dry rocky slopes. Occupies the dry disturbed areas in tundra like hummocks and pingos.

Arctic red fescue
Tribe: Poeae

appressed panicle inflorescence

florets

scabrous
panicle
branches

glumes

ligule

anthers

lemma

palea

hairy spikelet

Aleutian red fescue

Festuca rubra subsp. *aucta* (V.I. Krecz. & Bobrov) Hultén

Perennial, rhizomatous; narrow panicle inflorescence, when mature generally partly inserted in the uppermost sheath; leaves not boat tipped, blades involute and if flat, usually less than 3 mm wide (2-4); membranous ligule; auricles absent; spikelets several flowered, relatively small, laterally compressed to somewhat rounded on the back, not in 1-sided clusters; glumes shorter than the multiple fertile florets within them; lemma nerves converging at the summit, lemmas mostly glabrous, awns usually longer than 1.6 mm.

Plants perennial, rhizomatous, loosely tufted; culms up to 12 dm tall; mature inflorescence partly included in the uppermost sheath; cauline leaf blades flat to sometimes folded, not boat tipped, 2-4 mm wide; ligules membranous.

Narrow to open panicle inflorescence, often secund, to 25 cm long, branches often lax, scabrous; spikelets to 14 mm long, to 10 florets; glumes acute to acuminate, usually glabrous; lemmas to 9 mm long usually glabrous; awns usually 2.5-4.5 mm long; anthers usually 2.5-3.5 mm long.

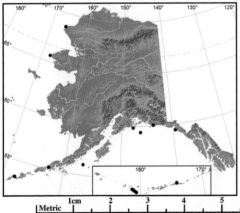

Native grass of coastal areas. Often present in stabilized sand dunes or beaches above high tide shorelines.

Aleutian red fescue
Tribe: Poeae

florets

appressed to open panicle inflorescence

spikelets

lemmas

paleas

anthers
2.5 -3.5 mm long

florets

ligule

glumes

Red fescue
Festuca rubra L. subsp. *rubra*

Perennial, rhizomatous; narrow panicle inflorescence, when mature generally exserted from the uppermost sheath, 7-12 cm long; leaves not boat tipped, blades involute and if flat, less than 2 mm wide; membranous ligule; auricles absent; spikelets several flowered, relatively small, laterally compressed to somewhat rounded on the back, not in 1-sided clusters; glumes shorter than the multiple fertile florets within them; lower glumes 3-4.5 mm long; lemma nerves converging at the summit, lemmas mostly glabrous, awns 0.6-4 mm long.

Plants perennial, rhizomatous, loosely tufted; culms to 9 dm tall; mature inflorescence exserted above the uppermost sheath; cauline leaf blades flat to usually folded, not boat tipped, less than 2 mm wide; ligules membranous.

Narrow to open panicle inflorescence, to 12 cm long, branches scabrous; spikelets to 14 mm long, to 8 florets; glumes 3-4.5 mm long, acute to acuminate, usually glabrous; lemmas to 8 mm long, usually glabrous; awns usually 0.6-4 mm long; anthers usually 2.5-3.5 mm long.

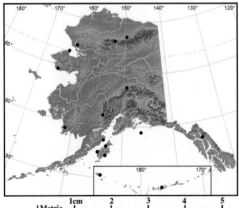

Native grass used for soil stabilization, lawns, and turf. Occupies gravelly sites, disturbances, and roadsides. A number of cultivars are widely used in Alaska for revegetation and erosion control.

Red fescue
Tribe: Poeae

panicle inflorescence

scabrous
inflorescence
branches

spikelet

ligule

florets

rachilla

florets

adaxial
leaf hairs

anthers

palea

glumes

lemma

glumes

Rock red fescue
Festuca rubra subsp. *pruinosa* (Hack.) Piper

Perennial, rhizomatous; narrow-panicle inflorescence, when mature generally exserted from the uppermost sheath, 3-10 cm long; leaves not boat tipped, blades involute and if flat, less than 2 mm wide; membranous ligule; auricles absent; spikelets several flowered, relatively small, laterally compressed to somewhat rounded on the back, not in 1-sided clusters; glumes shorter than the multiple fertile florets within them; lower glumes 2.2-3.2 mm long; lemma nerves converging at the summit, lemmas mostly glabrous, awns usually 0.4-3 mm long.

Plants perennial, rhizomatous, usually densely tufted; culms to 7 dm tall; mature inflorescence exserted above the uppermost sheath; cauline leaves usually folded, not boat tipped, less than 2 mm wide; ligules membranous.

Narrow, congested to open panicle inflorescence, generally 3-10 cm long, branches scabrous; spikelets to 14 mm long, up to 4-7 florets; glumes 2.2-3.2 mm long, acute to acuminate, usually glabrous; lemmas up to 8 mm long usually glabrous to scabrous near the apices; awns usually 0.4-3 mm long; anthers usually 2.3-3.2 mm long.

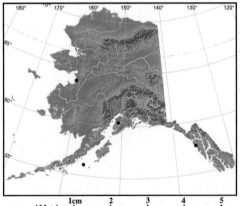

Native grass of coastal areas. Grows in rock crevices and pebble/sand beaches above the high tideline. Known as the coastal subspecies of the *Festuca rubra* complex.

Rock red fescue
Tribe: Poeae

panicle

appressed to open panicle inflorescence

palea

anthers

lemma

glumes

floret

rachilla

lemma

mostly glabrous branches

scabrous tip of lemma

scabrous tip of glumes

spikelet

glumes

panicle branch

Viviparous fescue

Festuca viviparoidea Krajina *ex* Pavlick

Festuca vivipara subsp. *glabra* Fred.

Perennial, densely tufted, without rhizomes; contracted-panicle inflorescence; ligule membranous; auricles absent; leaves not boat tipped, blades mostly folded, less than 3 mm wide; spikelets several flowered, pseudoviviparous, not in 1-sided clusters; glumes shorter than the included florets; lemma nerves converge at the smooth or scabrous apex, awns up to 1 mm long.

Plants perennial, densely tufted, without rhizomes; culms to 2.8 dm tall; blades to 1 mm in diameter, folded, not boat tipped; ligules membranous.

Panicle contracted, 1-2 branches per node, sometimes a raceme with single erect branches, usually 2+ spikelets per branch; spikelets pseudoviviparous, varying length; glumes and 1 or 2 lower lemmas may appear normal, distal florets replaced by expanded bracts; normal lemmas to 6 mm long; when awned, awns to 1 mm long; expanded and vegetative bracts unawned.

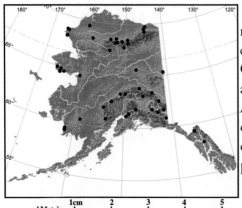

Native grass of drier mountain short willow communities and dry tundra. Often found on gravelly beaches and large gravel bars in rivers. Attempts have been made to commercialize this species and exploit the benefits of viviparous propagules for revegetation.

Viviparous fescue
Tribe: Poeae

panicle inflorescence

leaf like lemmas

florets

ligule

florets

spikelet

unequal glumes

Northern rough fescue, Altai fescue

Festuca altaica Trin.

Perennial, densely tufted, rarely with short rhizomes, tall, over 4 dm tall; open panicle inflorescence often secund; ligule membranous; auricles absent; leaves not boat tipped, blades mostly folded, usually to 4 mm wide, deciduous; spikelets several flowered, relatively small, not in 1-sided clusters, not pseudoviviparous; glumes shorter than the included florets; lemma nerves converging at summit, awns 0.2-0.7 mm long.

Plants perennial, densely tufted, rarely with short rhizomes, culms up to 12 dm tall; leaf blades deciduous, mostly folded, up to 2.5 mm in diameter, up to 4 mm wide when flat, not boat tipped; ligule membranous.

Panicle inflorescence, to 16 cm long, open, often secund, 1-2 branches per node; branches lax, spreading, lower branches usually recurved or reflexed, spikelets present towards the branch ends; spikelets up to 14 mm long, usually purple, to 6 florets; glumes distinctly shorter than the adjacent lemmas; lemmas to 12 mm long, veins converging at the tip, awns 0.2-0.7 mm long; anthers usually 2.6-4.5 mm long.

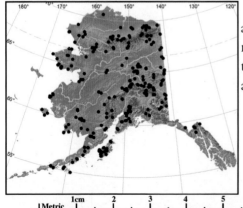

Native grass common across Alaska. Found on drier and rocky sites in the alpine, open dry tundra, open areas of the boreal and subalpine forests of Alaska.

Northern rough fescue, Altai fescue
Tribe: Poeae

open, lax and loosely erect panicle inflorescence

anther florets

paleas

lemmas

glumes

stigma

spikelets large
10-15 mm long

panicle
branch

spikelets

anthers
greater
than
1 mm
long

narrow
leaf blade

short
ligule

Western fescue
Festuca occidentalis Hook.

Perennial, densely to loosely tufted, without rhizomes, tall, over 4 dm tall; open and spreading panicle inflorescence, branches often reflexed; ligule membranous; auricles absent; leaves not boat tipped, blades folded, less than 3 mm wide; spikelets several flowered, relatively small, not in 1-sided clusters, not pseudoviviparous; glumes shorter than the included florets; lemma nerves converging at the summit, awns 3-12 mm long.

Plants perennial, tufted without rhizomes; culms to 11 dm tall; leaf blades less than 3 mm wide, folded, not boat tipped; auricles absent; ligule membranous.

Panicle inflorescence open, spreading, and lax, to 20 cm long; lower branches often reflexed at maturity, 1-2 per node, to 15 cm long; spikelets 3-5 florets, to 10 mm long, compressed, evenly distributed on inflorescence branches; glumes 2 and usually shorter than the lowest floret; lemmas to 6 mm long, conspicuously awned, awns to 12 mm long; anthers to 3 mm long.

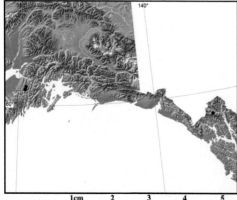

Native grass of dry to moist rocky open forest areas and along forest margins. Rather rare and appears to be isolated to southeastern Alaska.

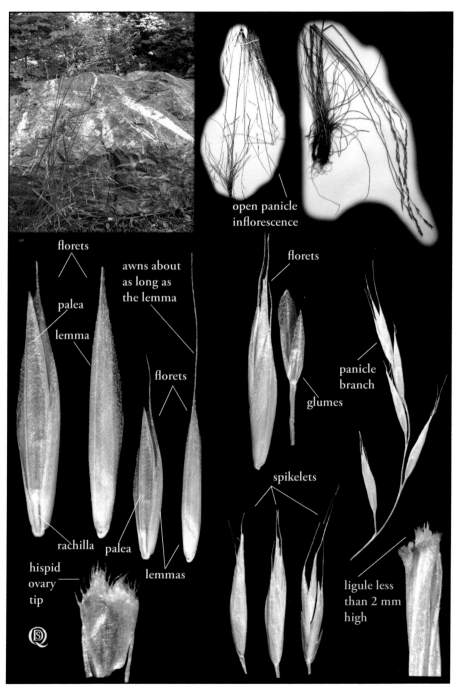

open panicle
inflorescence

florets

florets

awns about
as long as
the lemma

palea

lemma

florets

panicle
branch

glumes

florets

spikelets

rachilla   palea

lemmas

hispid
ovary
tip

ligule less
than 2 mm

Lena fescue

Festuca lenensis Drobow

Perennial, densely tufted, without rhizomes, usually less than 4 dm; narrow-appressed panicle inflorescence, green not glaucous colored; ligule membranous; auricles absent; leaves not boat tipped, blades folded, less than 3 mm wide; spikelets several flowered, relatively small, not in 1-sided clusters, not pseudoviviparous; glumes shorter than the included florets; lemma nerves converging at the summit, awns shorter than the lemmas; anthers 2-3.5 mm long.

Plants perennial, densely tufted; rhizomes absent; mostly green not glaucous; culms usually 1-3.5 dm tall, erect, mostly glabrous; leaf blades 0.4-1 mm in diameter; ligules membranous.

Panicle inflorescence, usually 1.5-4 cm long, erect, tightly appressed, 1-2 branches per node; branches stiff, erect, smooth or scabrous, lower branches with 1-2 spikelets; spikelets to 11 mm long, 3-6 florets, glumes exceeded by the florets within them; lower glumes 2.5-3.4 mm, upper glumes 3-4.3 mm long; lemmas 4-5.5 mm long, awns 0.8-3 mm long; anthers 2-3.5 mm long.

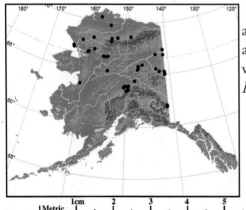

Native grass of dry, rocky, and often disturbed sites in alpine and low tundra habitat. *F. lenensis* was historically included as *F. ovina* in Alaska.

204

Lena fescue
Tribe: Poeae

appressed panicle inflorescence

inflorescence

anthers 2 mm or longer

palea as long as lemma

lemma

lemma

floret

glumes and lemmas scabrous near the apex

florets

glumes

spikelet

Baffin Island fescue
Festuca baffinensis Polunin

Perennial, densely tufted, without rhizomes, usually less than
4 dm tall, culms densely tomentose on the upper half; narrow appressed
panicle inflorescence; ligule membranous; auricles absent; leaves not boat
tipped, blades folded, less than 3 mm wide; spikelets several flowered,
relatively small, not in 1-sided clusters, not pseudoviviparous; glumes
shorter than the included florets; lemma nerves converging at the summit,
conspicuously awned, awns shorter than the lemmas; anthers
0.3-0.7 mm long.

Plants perennial, tufted; culms 0.8-1 dm tall, densely tomentose
on the upper half; leaf blades 0.4-0.6 mm wide, 4.5-7 cm long, folded,
involute; auricles absent; ligules membranous.

Panicle inflorescence, tightly flowered, usually 1.5-4 cm long;
spikelets 5.4-6 mm long, 3-4 florets; glumes 2.7-4.1 mm long, awnless;
lemmas 3.5-6 mm long, awned, the awn 0.5-2 mm long; anthers
0.3-0.7 mm long.

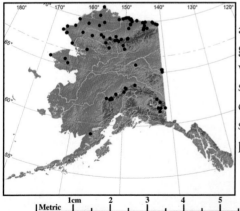

Native grass of the alpine
and arctic. Prefers moist exposed
gravelly soils of calcareous and
volcanic origin. Usually very short
stature. Often growing fully
exposed to wind, drought, poor
soils and cold where few other
plant species survive.

Baffin Island fescue

Tribe: Poeae

appressed panicle inflorescence

anther 0.3 mm
to 0.7 mm long

glumes

florets

hairy
floret
tip

short
ligule

spikelet

hairy
culm
below
inflorescence

inflorescence

207

Rocky Mountain fescue; Mountain fescue

Festuca saximontana Rydb.

Perennial, usually densely tufted, without rhizomes, culms often to 4 dm tall, glabrous, sometimes scabrous on the upper half; narrow appressed or contracted-panicle inflorescence, usually over 5 cm long; ligule membranous; auricles absent; leaves not boat tipped, blades folded, involute, less than 3 mm wide; spikelets several flowered, relatively small, not in 1-sided clusters, not pseudoviviparous; glumes shorter than the included florets; lemma nerves converging at the summit, conspicuously awned, awns shorter than the lemmas, 1-2 mm long; anthers usually 1.2-1.7 mm long.

Plants perennial, tufted; culms 1.5-4 dm tall; leaves folded, blades involute; auricles absent; ligules membranous.

Panicle a narrow, compressed inflorescence, tightly flowered, usually over 5 cm long; spikelets usually 4.5-8 mm long, 3-5-flowered; glumes shorter than the included florets, the first 1.5-3.5 mm long, the second 2.5-4.8 mm long; lemmas 3.4-4.5 mm long, glabrous, smooth to scaberulous distally, awns 1-2 mm long; anthers usually 1.2-1.7 mm long.

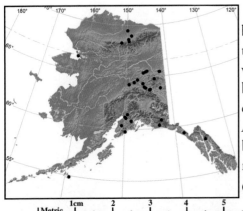

Native grass that has likely been misidentified as *F. ovina* in the field. Also likely confused with *F. lenensis* which appears to be more common at higher elevations and in the dry tundra of Alaska. *F. saximontana* appears to be more common in the neighboring Yukon Territory of Canada.

Rocky Mountain fescue; Mountain fescue

Tribe: Poeae

panicle inflorescence

lemma awns

anthers over 1 mm long

spikelet

anther

palea

ligule

lemma

florets

upper glume

lower glume

rachilla

glumes

Alpine fescue; Sheep fescue
Festuca brachyphylla Schult. & Schult. f.

Festuca ovina var. *brevifolia* S. Watson

Perennial, usually densely tufted, without rhizomes, culms to about 3 dm tall, glabrous, sometimes scabrous on the upper half; narrow appressed or contracted panicle inflorescence usually to 4 cm long; ligule membranous; auricles absent; leaves not boat tipped, blades folded, involute, less than 3 mm wide, blade of the flag leaf sheath usually not inflated; spikelets several flowered, relatively small, not in 1-sided clusters, not pseudoviviparous; glumes shorter than the included florets; lemma nerves converging at the summit, conspicuously awned, awns shorter than the lemmas, 1-3 mm long; anthers usually 0.7-1.1 mm long.

Plants perennial, tufted; culms to about 3 dm tall; leaves folded, blades involute, blade of the flag leaf usually 1-2.5 cm long, sheath usually not inflated; auricles absent; ligules membranous.

Panicle inflorescence narrow, contracted, usually 1.5-4 cm long, 1-2 branches per node, rarely single branches or a raceme; loosely flowered; spikelets several flowered and relatively small, compressed to rounded on the back; glumes 2 and usually shorter than the lowest floret; lemmas usually 2.5-4.5 mm long, conspicuously awned, awns 1-3 mm long; anthers usually 0.7-1.1 mm long.

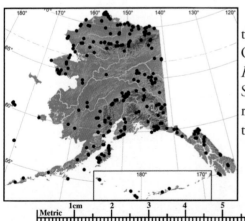

Native grass common to the alpine and dry sites of tundra. Often confused with *F. lenensis* and *F. saximontana*, but not as tall. Sheep fescue has been used for revegetating disturbed sites throughout Alaska.

210

Alpine fescue; Sheep fescue
Tribe: Poeae

spikelets

appressed panicle inflorescence

panicle branch

anther usually less than 1.1 mm long

florets

lemmas

palea

florets

ligule

glumes

Little fescue; Small-flowered fescue
Festuca minutiflora Rydb.

Perennial, loosely to densely tufted, without rhizomes, culms to about 3 dm tall, glabrous; narrow appressed or contracted panicle inflorescence to about 4 cm long, branching more than once; ligule membranous; auricles absent; leaves not boat tipped, blades folded, involute, less than 3 mm wide, foliage fine and bristlelike, sheaths usually distinctly inflated; spikelets several flowered, relatively small, not in 1-sided clusters, not pseudoviviparous; glumes shorter than the included florets; lemma nerves converging at the summit, 2.2-3.5 mm long, conspicuously awned, awns shorter than the lemmas, 0.5-1.5 mm long; anthers usually to 1.2 mm long.

Plants perennial, loosely to densely tufted; culms to about 3 dm tall; leaves folded, blades involute, foliage fine and bristlelike, blade of the flag leaf usually 0.7-3.5 cm long, sheaths usually distinctly inflated; auricles absent; ligules membranous.

Inflorescence a narrow panicle, usually branching more than once, 1-2 branches to a node, to about 4 cm long; spikelets 3-5 mm long, usually 3-4 florets; glumes shorter than the included florets, the first 1.5-2 mm long, the second 2.2-2.7 mm long; lemmas 2.2-3.5 mm long, awns 0.5-1.5 mm long; anthers usually 0.6-1.2 mm long.

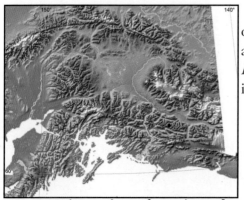

Native cool season grass of mountain alpine and subalpine areas. Rare in Alaska, similar to *F. brachyphylla,* and often included in *F. ovina.*

Little fescue; Small-flowered fescue

inflorescence an appressed panicle

florets

florets

anthers 0.6-1.2 mm long

glumes

spikelets

rachilla

hairy tip
of ovary

Short fescue

Festuca brevissima Jurtsev
Festuca ovina subsp. *alaskana* Holmen

 Perennial, densely tufted, without rhizomes, culms usually to
1.5 dm tall, mostly glabrous, erect, over 2 times the height of the basal
tuft of leaves; narrow appressed or contracted panicle inflorescence to
about 5 cm long, usually single branches from a node (raceme); ligule
membranous; auricles absent; leaves not boat tipped, blades folded,
involute less than 3 mm wide, foliage not fine and bristlelike, sheaths
usually distinctly inflated; spikelets several flowered, relatively small, not
in 1-sided clusters, not pseudoviviparous; glumes shorter than the
included florets; lemma nerves converging at the summit, usually
4-5.5 mm long, conspicuously awned, awns shorter than the lemmas,
0.5-2.5 mm long; anthers usually 0.9-1.2 mm long.

 Plants perennial, densely tufted; culms to about 1.5 dm tall; leaves
folded, blades involute, foliage not fine and bristlelike, blade of the flag
leaf usually 0.2-1 cm long, sheaths usually distinctly inflated; auricles
absent; ligules membranous.

 Inflorescence a narrow panicle, usually a single branch at a node,
to about 5 cm long; spikelets 5-7 mm long, usually 2-4 florets; glumes
shorter than the included florets, the first 2.5-3.2 mm long, the second
3.2-4.8 mm long; lemmas usually 4-5.5 mm long, awns usually
0.5-2.5 mm long; anthers usually 0.9-1.2 mm long.

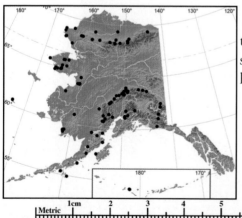

Native grass of alpine and
tundra. Recognized as being very
short and growing in rocky
habitat.

214

Short fescue
Tribe: Poeae

inflorescence

ligule

inflorescence an appressed panicle

anther 0.9-1.2 mm long

florets

lemmas

palea

florets

spikelets

rachilla

glumes

Edlund's fescue

Festuca edlundiae S. Aiken, Consaul & Lefk.

Perennial, densely tufted, without rhizomes, culms usually to 1 dm high, mostly glabrous, usually geniculate to prostate, to 2 times the height of the basal tuft of leaves if erect; narrow appressed or contracted panicle inflorescence to about 4 cm long, 1 or 2 branches from a node, often a single branch (raceme); ligule membranous; auricles absent; leaves not boat tipped, blades folded, involute less than 3 mm wide, foliage not fine and bristlelike, sheaths distinctly inflated; spikelets several flowered, relatively small, not in 1-sided clusters, not pseudoviviparous; glumes shorter than the included florets; lemma nerves converging at the summit, to 5.2 mm long, conspicuously awned, awns shorter than the lemmas, 1.1-2.9 mm long; anthers usually 0.6-1.1 mm long.

Plants perennial, densely tufted; culms to about 1 dm tall; leaves folded, blades involute, foliage not fine and bristlelike, blade of the flag leaf usually 0.5-2 cm long, sheaths usually distinctly inflated; auricles absent; ligules membranous.

Inflorescence a narrow panicle, 1 or 2 branches at a node, often a raceme, to about 4 cm long; spikelets 4.5-8.5 mm long, usually 3-6 florets; glumes shorter than the included florets, the first 1.8-3.5 mm long, the second 2.9-4.3 mm long; lemmas 3.6-5.2 mm long, awns 1.1-2.9 mm long; anthers 0.6-1.1mm long.

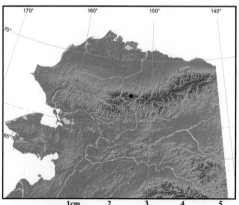

Native grass of alpine and dry tundra. Appears to favor calcareous and fine substrates. Has been included in *F. ovina*.

Edlund's fescue
Tribe: Poeae

compressed panicle inflorescence

florets

lemma

branch

florets

glabrous
ovary

paleas

anthers

rachillas

glumes

spikelet

Annual bluegrass

Poa annua L.

Annual; open-panicle inflorescence; membranous ligule; boat-tipped leaves; spikelets relatively small, laterally compressed, not in 1-sided clusters, glumes shorter than multiple florets within them; glumes and lemmas not awned; lemma nerves converging towards the tip.

Plants annual; culms usually 0.2-2 dm tall, smooth, glabrous; sheaths open, smooth, glabrous; blades usually 1-3 mm wide, 1-10 cm long, flat or folded, boat tipped, glabrous; auricles absent; ligules membranous, usually 0.5-3 mm long.

Panicle pyramidal, open, usually 1-7 cm long; spikelets with 2-6 florets, crowded, 3-5 mm long; first glume 1.5-2 mm long, 1-nerved; second glume 2-2.5 mm long, 3-nerved; lemmas compressed-keeled, not webbed at the base, 2.5-4 mm long, distinctly 5-nerved, more or less pubescent on the lower half of nerves, long basal hairs on the lower part of keel, sometimes weblike; anthers 0.6-1.1 mm long.

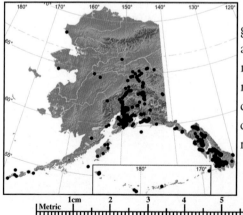

Introduced early growing grass found in moist and disturbed areas within meadows and other riparian zones. Also found along roadsides, in parking lots, and campgrounds. This species is considered an agricultural pest and much effort is spent trying to control and prevent its spread.

Annual bluegrass
Tribe: Poeae

anthers 0.6-1.1 mm long

open panicle inflorescence

panicle branch

crowded spikelets

lower glume 1-nerved

glumes

florets

palea

lemma

nerves hairy

spikelets

ligule

annual plant roots

Hartz's bluegrass
Poa hartzii subsp. *alaskana* Soreng

Perennial, tufted to loosely tufted, culms usually decumbent; panicle inflorescence usually appressed or contracted, longer than wide, lower branches usually more than 2 per node; membranous ligule 5-7 mm long; boat-tipped leaves; spikelets not in 1-sided clusters, relatively small, 4.8-7.4 mm long, somewhat laterally compressed, glumes shorter than multiple florets within them; glumes and lemmas not awned; lemmas 5.5-7 mm long, weakly keeled, nerves converging toward the tip, loose to densely hairy over the lower ½, hairs usually longer than 0.5 mm.

Plants perennial, loosely tufted; culms 2-4.5 dm tall, usually decumbent; blades 1.5-3 mm wide, folded or involute, boat tipped; auricles absent; ligules membranous, 5-7 mm long, obtuse, acuminate, decurrent.

Panicle inflorescence, erect, contracted or narrowly ovate; often congested with 7-40 spikelets, 2-4 branches per lower nodes; spikelets 4.8-7.4 mm long, length 3.5-4 times width, weakly laterally compressed; lemmas usually 5.5-7 mm long, weakly keeled, somewhat densely hairy over the proximal ½; anthers if developed 2-2.8 mm long.

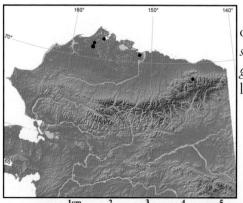

Native grass of high arctic open sandy sites. Resembles *P. secunda* subsp. *secunda* and *P. glauca* subsp. *glauca,* but is more loosely tufted. Rather rare.

Hartz's bluegrass
Tribe: Poeae

R.J. Soreng

R.J. Soreng

R.J. Soreng

appressed to open panicle inflorescence   Meade River

anthers   stigma

palea

lemma

floret

panicle
branches

spikelets

ligule

florets

glumes

Big bluegrass

Poa secunda subsp. *juncifolia* (Scribn.) Soreng
Poa ampla Merr.

Perennial, tufted; inflorescence an appressed panicle, about 2 cm wide; blades soft, flat, boat tipped, 1-3 mm wide, 2-25 cm long; membranous ligule, 1.5-5 mm long, not decurrent; spikelets not in 1-sided clusters, dorsally compressed; both glumes shorter than the multiple perfect florets within them; lemmas rounded on the back, keels obscure, glabrous, nerves converging towards the tip so somewhat acutely pointed, awnless.

Plants perennial, tufted; culms 6.1-12.2 dm tall, hollow, smooth, glabrous, glaucous; vernation folded; sheaths open, smooth, glabrous; blades 1-3 mm wide, 2-25 cm long, flat to folded, boat tipped; auricles absent; ligules membranous, 1.5-5 mm long, obtuse, ciliolate, puberulent abaxially.

Panicle 10-15 cm long, narrow, usually dense and often 2 cm wide; spikelets 3- to 8-flowered, 6-10 mm long; glumes 3-nerved, first glume 3-4 mm long, second glume 4-5 mm long; lemmas rounded on the back, not keeled, not webbed, 4-6 mm long, smooth or minutely scabrous; anthers 1.5-3 mm long.

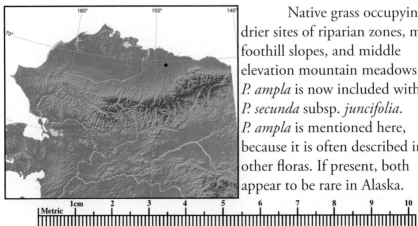

Native grass occupying drier sites of riparian zones, moist foothill slopes, and middle elevation mountain meadows. *P. ampla* is now included with *P. secunda* subsp. *juncifolia*. *P. ampla* is mentioned here, because it is often described in other floras. If present, both appear to be rare in Alaska.

Big bluegrass

Tribe: Poeae

stigma
anther

appressed panicle inflorescence branch spikelets

florets

rather flat leaf blades

lemma

florets in flower

dorsally compressed spikelets

ligule

Canby bluegrass

Poa secunda J. Presl subsp. *secunda*

Poa canbyi (Scribn.) Howell

Perennial, tufted; inflorescence a narrow and appressed panicle; culms more than 3 dm tall, upright; blades soft, boat tipped, 15-30 cm long; ligule membranous; spikelets not in 1-sided clusters, dorsally compressed, 6-10 mm long; both glumes shorter than the multiple perfect florets within them; lemmas rounded on the back, keels obscure, crisp-puberulent on the back toward the base, pubescence sometimes obscure, nerves somewhat converging towards the tip so somewhat acutely pointed, awnless.

Plants perennial, tufted; culms 4.6-12.2 dm tall, smooth, glabrous; blades 1-3 mm wide, 15-30 cm long, folded, boat tipped; auricles absent; ligules membranous, 1.7-4.1 mm long, obtuse, entire or lacerate, glabrous or puberulent abaxially.

Panicle narrow, compact or rather loose, 10-20 cm long, usually over 1 cm wide, often pale, the branches short, appressed; spikelets 3- to 5-flowered, 6-10 mm long; glumes narrow, first glume 3.5-4 mm long, 1-nerved or obscurely 3-nerved, second glume slightly longer, 3-nerved; lemmas rounded on back, not keeled, not webbed, 4-5 mm long, somewhat crisp-puberulent on the lower part of the back: anthers 1.5-3 mm long.

Native grass of higher elevation foothills and mountains. *P. canbyi*, is now included in *P. secunda* subsp. *secunda,* from which it differs by having longer and more robust leaf material. *P. canbyi* is mentioned here, because it is often described in other floras. If present, both appear to be rare in Alaska.

Canby bluegrass

Tribe: Poeae

appressed panicle
inflorescence branch
spikelets

dorsally
compressed
spikelets

ligule

pubescent
lemmas

glumes

Colorado bluegrass; Narrow-flower bluegrass

Poa stenantha Trin.
Poa macroclada Rydb.

Perennial, tufted, culm upright, bases decumbent or sometimes erect; appressed to spreading-panicle inflorescence, longer than wide, lower branches usually more than 2 per node; membranous ligule 2-5 mm long; boat-tipped leaves; spikelets relatively small, 6-10 mm long, somewhat compressed, not in 1-sided clusters, for a *Poa* the spikelet is much longer than wide, somewhat rounded on the back of the lemmas; glumes shorter than multiple florets within them; glumes and lemmas not awned, nerves converging towards the tip; lemmas 4-6 mm long, callus with a crown of hairs, pubescent on the keel, marginal nerves or both, sometimes on the internerves as well.

Plants perennial, tufted; culms usually 2-6 dm tall, bases erect or decumbent; blades 1.5-5 mm wide, folded or involute, boat tipped; auricles absent; ligules membranous, 2-5 mm long, obtuse, entire or erose, ciliolate, puberulent abaxially.

Panicle open, 5-25 cm long, pyramidal, the branches spreading, distant in 2's or 3's, as much as 8 cm long, naked on the lower half or two-thirds; spikelets about 6-10 mm long, acute, widest ⅔ from the base, 2-3 florets, purple; glumes 3.5-6.5 mm long; lemmas 4-6 mm long, pubescent on the keel and marginal nerves, callus with a crown of hairs, 0.2-2 mm long; anthers 1.2-2 mm long.

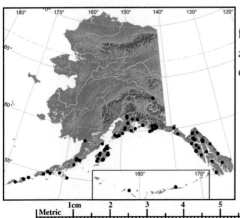

Native riparian zone grass found along the southern coastal areas, forest openings, gravel bars of streams, and meadows.

Colorado bluegrass; Narrow-flower bluegrass

Tribe: Poeae

fresh water streams near seacoast

panicle inflorescence

scabrous panicle branches

florets

palea

florets

panicle branch

upper glume

3 nerve lower glume

spikelets

lemma

ligule

crown of hair on the callus

glumes

Canada bluegrass

Poa compressa L.

Perennial, rhizomatous; inflorescence a narrow panicle 3-8 cm long, branches usually in 2's, spikelet-bearing to base; culms conspicuously flattened; leaves boat tipped; ligule membranous; spikelets relatively small, compressed, not in 1-sided clusters; glumes shorter than the multiple florets within them, glumes and lemmas usually keeled to the base, lemma nerves converging towards the tip, awnless.

Plants perennial, rhizomatous; culms 1.5-2 dm tall, flattened; blades 1-4 mm wide, 2-10 cm long, flat, folded or loosely involute, boat tipped; auricles absent; ligules membranous, 0.5-1.5 mm long, obtuse, ciliolate, puberulent abaxially.

Inflorescence a narrow panicle 3-8 cm long, branches usually in 2's, spikelet-bearing to base; spikelets 3- to 8-flowered, 4-6 mm long, crowded, subsessile; first glume 2-3 mm long, acute, second glume slightly longer and broader than the first; lemmas 2-3 mm long, compressed-keeled, web scant or absent, keel and marginal nerves slightly pubescent, glabrous between, awnless; anthers 1.3-1.8 mm long.

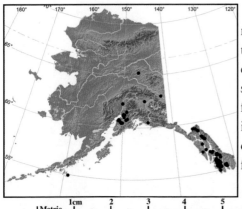

Considered to be either native or introduced. Common to disturbed areas like roadsides, campgrounds, and moist to drier soils of riparian zones. Not used for revegetation to any significance in Alaska. May have been a contaminant in other seed used for revegetation.

Canada bluegrass

Tribe: Poeae

inflorescence

panicle branch and spikelets

open panicle inflorescence

callus web

florets

callus web

glumes

spikelets

cross-section of flat culm

ligule

Eminent bluegrass

Poa eminens J. Presl

Perennial, rhizomatous, rhizomes stout, 2 mm thick; culms usually solitary, usually round; inflorescence a loosely contracted panicle, somewhat congested with 40-100+ spikelets; branches 3-10 cm long, ascending with 5-20 spikelets; leaves boat tipped; ligule membranous; spikelets relatively small, compressed, not in 1-sided clusters; glumes subequal to the multiple florets within them; lemmas laterally compressed, usually keeled to the base, nerves converging towards the tip, internerves glabrous or somewhat pubescent, awnless; anthers 1.1 mm or longer.

Plants perennial with stout rhizomes, 2 mm thick; culms usually solitary, 2-10 dm tall, terete; blades 5-10 mm wide, flat, thick, boat tipped; ligules 1-3.5 mm long, yellow-brown, truncate, erose, ciliolate.

Panicles 8-30 cm long, somewhat contracted, congested with 40-100+ spikelets; branches 3-10 cm long, ascending with 5-20 spikelets; spikelets 5-12 mm, laterally compressed, 2-6 florets; glumes subequal or the upper glumes to 2 mm longer than the lower glumes, may exceed the lowest lemmas; lower lemmas with a crown of hairs on the callus, hairs 1-2 mm long, lemmas 4.5-7 mm long, keeled, awnless; anthers 1.7-3.2 mm long.

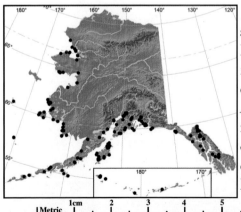

Native grass common to subsaline coastal areas and beaches. Found with coastal sedges and rushes. Rarely found in well established stands of *Leymus mollis*. Appears to be an excellent choice for reclamation and stabilization of disturbed coastal habitats, but commercial field production trials have failed.

230

Eminent bluegrass

Tribe: Poeae

large rhizomes

ligule

appressed
panicle
branch

open panicle inflorescence

palea

lemmas

florets

spikelets

glumes

Large-glume bluegrass

Poa macrocalyx Trautv. & C.A. Mey.

P. hispidula Vasey, *P. norbergii* Hultén., *P. turneri* Scribn.

Perennial, rhizomatous, rhizomes may be poorly developed, densely to loosely tufted, culms rounded; inflorescence a loosely contracted to open panicle, moderately congested with 20-100 spikelets, often nodding; branches 3-8 cm long, ascending to open with 5-15 spikelets crowded to the distal end; leaves boat tipped; ligule membranous; spikelets relatively small, compressed, not in 1-sided clusters, 2-5 florets; glumes subequal to the multiple florets within them; calluses dorsally webbed; lemmas laterally compressed, awnless, usually keeled to base, nerves converging toward tip, lacking lanate hairs between keel and nerves; anthers 1.1 mm or longer.

Plants perennial, tufted to loosely tufted, rhizomes sometimes poorly developed; culms, 3-12 dm tall, somewhat stout, mostly terete, erect to decumbent, usually not solitary; blades 4-12 cm long, 3-7 mm wide, flat, boat-tipped, loosely folded; ligules 2-5 mm long.

Panicles 4-20 cm long, lax, loosely appressed to open, moderately congested with spikelets, often nodding; branches 2-5 per node, 3-8 cm long, ascending, spikelets crowded at the end; spikelets 6-9 mm long; glumes subequal, usually nearly equaling the adjacent lemmas; calluses webbed, hairs copious and to ⅔ the length of the lemmas; lemmas 5-8 mm long, keeled, awnless; anthers 1.5-2.5 mm long.

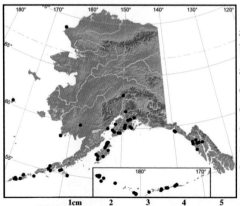

Native grass of coastal areas. Usually found on rocky beaches, as well as on gravelly and sandy shorelines, but usually occupies areas inland from the coastal fore-dunes. Has been commercialized and used on a limited number of erosion control and revegetation seedings in Alaska.

Large-glume bluegrass
Tribe: Poeae

open panicle inflorescence

seacoast habitat

palea

lemma

florets

viviparous form

branch

spikelets

florets

branches

large spikelets

ligule

upper glume

lower glume

233

Lax-flower bluegrass
Poa laxiflora Buckley

Perennial, rhizomatous, usually long rhizomes, culms solitary to loosely tufted, usually round; inflorescence a lax, open spreading panicle, sparse, 1-3 branches per node, branches to 15 cm long with 3-13 spikelets; culm sheaths retrorsely scabrous; leaves boat tipped; ligule membranous; spikelets relatively small, compressed, to 4 florets, not in 1-sided clusters; glumes shorter than the multiple florets within them; calluses webbed; lemmas laterally compressed, awnless, usually keeled to base, nerves converging toward tip, lacking lanate hairs between keel and nerves; anthers to 1.1 mm long.

Plants perennial, rhizomatous, rhizomes usually long, mostly solitary culms to loosely tufted; culms 5-12 dm tall; sheaths closed to ¾ their length, retrorsely scabrous; blades 3-8 mm wide, flat, lax, boat-tipped; ligules 2-3.5 mm long, obtuse to acute.

Panicles 14-30 cm long, open, sparse, 1-3 branches per node; branches to 15 cm long, spreading, mostly straight with 3-13 spikelets; spikelets to 8 mm long, laterally compressed, to 4 florets; glumes shorter than the adjacent lemmas; calluses webbed; lemmas to 6 mm long, distinctly keeled, keels hairy to ¾ their length, awnless; anthers 0.5-1.1 mm long.

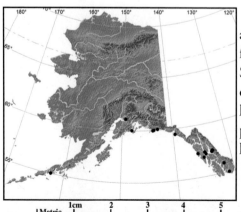

Native grass of shaded and moist coastal spruce/hemlock forests of Southeast and Southcentral Alaska. Rare and often overlooked, because its highly rhizomatous growth form produces solitary culms, or is loosely tufted.

Lax-flower bluegrass

Tribe: Poeae

R.J. Soreng

R.J. Soreng

florets

open and lax panicle inflorescence

lemma

spikelets

palea

ligule

glumes

glabrous
lemma
keel

lemma

lax and
open
panicle

scabrous
panicle
branch

panicle
branches

scabrous
palea edges

palea

webbed
lemma

Kentucky bluegrass
Poa pratensis subsp. *colpodea* (Th. Fr.) Tzvelev

Perennial, extensively rhizomatous; densely to loosely tufted, culms sometimes solitary, usually round; inflorescence generally a loosely contracted to open pyramidal panicle, often congested with several spikelets from 2-5 branches per node; culm sheaths glabrous to sometimes hairy; leaves boat tipped; ligule membranous; spikelets relatively small, compressed, 2-5 florets, some bulbiferous, not in 1-sided clusters; glumes shorter than the multiple florets within them; calluses distinctly webbed; lemmas laterally compressed, awnless, usually keeled to base, nerves converging toward tip, lacking lanate hairs between keel and nerves; anthers 1.1 mm or longer when present, of the high-arctic tundra.

Plants perennial, rhizomatous, densely to loosely tufted, strongly anthocyanic; culms mostly solitary, 1.5-3 dm tall; basal innovation shoot blades to 15 cm long, to 3.6 mm wide, boat tipped, ligule membranous, 0.9-3 mm long.

Panicle loosely contracted or narrowly pyramidal, 4-8 cm long, 2-5 branches per node, 1-3 cm long, smooth to sparsely scabrous, several spikelets per branch; spikelets bulbiferous, least deformed to 5 mm long; glume and lemma keels distinct; florets mostly bulb-forming; anthers usually aborted.

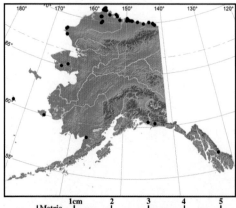

Native grass of the high Arctic. Often found on dry tundra and disturbed sites. The common Kentucky bluegrass species of arctic coastal plains.

Kentucky bluegrass
Tribe: Poeae

panicle inflorescence

panicle branches

florets

bulblet florets

glumes

normal floret

ligule

spikelets

Alpigene bluegrass

Poa pratensis subsp. ***alpigena*** (Lindm.) Hiitonen
Poa alpigena Lindm.

Perennial, extensively rhizomatous; moderately to loosely tufted, culms usually solitary, usually round; inflorescence generally a loosely contracted to open pyramidal panicle, often congested with 5-15 spikelets per branch, usually with 2-5 branches per node, branches smooth or mostly smooth; culm sheaths glabrous to sometimes hairy; leaves boat tipped; ligule membranous; spikelets relatively small, compressed, 2-5 florets, none bulbiferous, not in 1-sided clusters; glumes shorter than the multiple florets within them; calluses distinctly webbed; lemmas laterally compressed, awnless, usually keeled to base, nerves converging toward tip, lacking lanate hairs between keel and nerves; anthers 1.1 mm or longer.

Plants perennial, rhizomatous, moderately to loosely tufted, strongly anthocyanic, culms mostly solitary; culms 1.5-7 dm tall; basal innovation shoot blades to 15 cm long, to 3.6 mm wide, boat-tipped, ligule membranous, 0.9-3 mm long.

Panicle contracted or narrowly pyramidal, expanding at maturity, 3-13 cm long, 2-5 branches per node, 1-6 cm long, usually smooth, 5-15 spikelets per branch, eventually spreading to reflexed; spikelets not bulbiferous, 4-5.5 mm long; lemmas 2.5-3.3 mm long, lateral veins short-villous to softly puberulent; anthers 1.2-2 mm long.

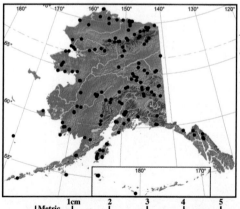

Native grass found across Alaska. Often growing in the same locality as *P. pratensis* subsp. *colpodea,* but is not viviparous. Both sub-species are native.

Alpigene bluegrass
Tribe: Poeae

open panicle inflorescence

lemma
palea

florets

1st glume
narrow

2-5 panicle
branches
per node

panicle branches smooth

2nd glume wide
palea   florets

anthers   stigma

palea
lemma
web

rachilla

lax and soft
leaves

Kentucky bluegrass
Poa pratensis subsp. *angustifolia* (L.) Lej.
Poa angustifolia L.

Perennial, extensively rhizomatous; moderately to loosely tufted, intravaginal shoots clustered, culms usually round; inflorescence generally contracted or a narrowly pyramidal panicle, usually with 2-5 branches per node, branches scabrous, several to many spikelets per branch; culm sheaths glabrous to sometimes hairy; leaves somewhat stiff, folded to involute, boat tipped; ligule membranous; spikelets relatively small, compressed, 2-5 florets, none bulbiferous, not in 1-sided clusters; glumes shorter than the multiple florets within them; calluses distinctly webbed; lemmas laterally compressed, awnless, usually keeled to base, nerves converging toward tip, lacking lanate hairs between keel and nerves; anthers 1.1 mm or longer.

Plants perennial, rhizomatous, moderately to loosely tufted, strongly anthocyanic, culms mostly solitary; culms 2.5-8 dm tall; basal branching intra- and extravaginal, intravaginal shoots clustered; basal innovation shoot blades to 45 cm long, 1 mm wide, firm, folded to involute, boat tipped, ligule membranous, 0.9-3 mm long.

Panicle, 8-18 cm long, 2-5 branches per node, usually scabrous, several to many spikelets per branch; spikelets not bulbiferous; glume and lemma keels distinct and strongly compressed; calluses distinctly webbed; lemmas 2.5-3.5 mm long, lateral veins glabrous; anthers 1.2-2 mm long.

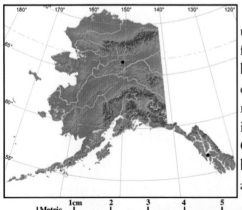

Introduced grass often used for lawns and turf. Was used for reclamation of disturbed sites, but this practice is now discouraged and plantings are now limited to landscaping in urban and developed areas. Often eliminates native grasses because it is strongly rhizomatous and sod forming.

240

Kentucky bluegrass
Tribe: Poeae

open panicle inflorescence

panicle branches

florets

palea

lemma

stigma

spikelets

glumes

folded or stiff leaves

glumes

stigma

palea

florets

lemmas

anthers

callus
web of hairs

241

Kentucky bluegrass
Poa pratensis L. subsp. *pratensis*

Perennial, extensively rhizomatous; densely to loosely tufted, often forming sod, usually green; intravaginal shoots clustered, culms usually round; inflorescence generally an open pyramidal panicle, usually with 3-5 branches per node, spreading to reflexed, branches scabrous, several to many spikelets per branch; culm sheaths glabrous to sometimes hairy; leaves somewhat soft, flat to folded, boat tipped; ligule membranous; spikelets relatively small, compressed, 2-5 florets, none bulbiferous, not in 1-sided clusters; glumes shorter than the multiple florets within them; calluses distinctly webbed; lemmas laterally compressed, awnless, usually keeled to base, nerves converging toward tip, lacking lanate hairs between keel and nerves; anthers 1.1 mm or longer.

Plants perennial, strongly rhizomatous, often forming sod; culms 8-10 dm tall; basal branching intra- and extravaginal, intravaginal shoots clustered; basal innovation shoot blades to 45 cm long, 4 mm wide, flat or folded, boat tipped; ligules membranous, 0.4-0.6 mm long.

Inflorescence an open, spreading pyramidal panicle, 5-18 cm long, to 7 branches per node, scabrous; spikelets 3-5 florets, 3-6 mm long; glumes shorter than the lemmas within them, 3-3.5 mm long; lemmas compressed, webbed at base, about 3-3.5 mm long, midnerve and marginal nerves pubescent, intermediate nerves glabrous, awnless.

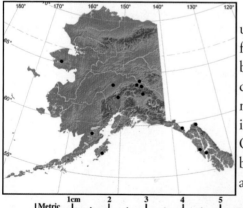

Introduced grass often used for lawns and turf. Was used for reclamation of disturbed sites, but this practice is now discouraged and plantings are now limited to landscaping in urban and developed areas. Often eliminates native grasses because it is strongly rhizomatous and sod forming.

Kentucky bluegrass
Tribe: Poeae

rhizomes

open panicle inflorescence
spikelets

ligule

anthers

strongly
compressed
spikelet

webbing
at the base
of the lemmas

glumes

Kentucky bluegrass

Poa pratensis subsp. *irrigata* (Lindm.) H. Lindb.

Poa subcaerulea Sm.

Perennial, extensively rhizomatous; moderately to loosely tufted, may form sod, usually glaucous; mostly extravaginal branching, culms usually round; inflorescence generally an open pyramidal panicle, usually with 1-2 branches per node, 1.5-6 cm long, spreading to reflexed, branches scabrous, 4-8 spikelets per branch; culm sheaths glabrous to sometimes hairy; leaves soft, boat tipped; ligule membranous; spikelets relatively small, compressed, 3-5 florets, none bulbiferous, not in 1-sided clusters; glumes shorter than the multiple florets within them; calluses distinctly webbed; lemmas laterally compressed, awnless, usually keeled to base, nerves converging toward tip, lacking lanate hairs between keel and nerves; anthers 1.1 mm or longer.

Plants perennial, strongly rhizomatous, often forming sod; culms 0.8-5 dm tall; basal branching mostly extravaginal, basal innovation shoot blades to 15 cm long, 4.5 mm wide, flat or folded, boat tipped; ligules membranous.

Inflorescence an open, often spreading pyramidal panicle, 2-10 cm long, usually 1-2 branches per node; spikelets 3-5 florets, glumes shorter than the lemmas within them; lemmas compressed-keeled, webbed at base, to 6 mm long, finely muriculate, lateral veins glabrous, awnless.

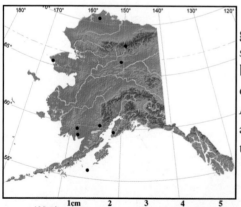

Native grass that is generally shorter than other subspecies of *P. pratensis*. Panicle branches are stiff and generally only 1 or 2 branches per node. Appears to be mostly a coastal and glaucous colored subspecies that needs further study.

Kentucky bluegrass
Tribe: Poeae

panicle inflorescence mostly
2 branches per node

glaucous color

lemma

branch

palea

spikelets

floret

glumes

Roughstalk bluegrass

Poa trivialis L.

Perennial, tufted, may be weakly stoloniferous; spreading-panicle inflorescence; culms up to 10 dm tall, usually round; membranous ligule; boat-tipped leaves; spikelets relatively small, ovate, 3-4.5 mm long, compressed, not in 1-sided clusters; glumes shorter than the multiple florets within them, 1st glume narrow and curved, sickle-shaped; glumes and lemmas awnless; lemmas sericeous on the keel, sometimes puberulent on the marginal nerves, webbed at base, nerve between the keel and marginal nerve very prominent, usually keeled to base, nerves converging toward tip; anthers 1.1 mm or longer.

Plants perennial, tufted usually weakly stoloniferous; culms 4-10 dm tall, erect or decumbent, smooth, puberulent around nodes; blades 15-20 cm long, 1.7-5 mm wide, flat, boat tipped, auricles absent; ligules membranous, 1.6-2.7 mm long, obtuse, ciliolate, glabrous.

Panicles 6-14 cm long, loose, oblong, the branches ascending, the lower ones usually in groups of 5; spikelets 3-4.5 mm long, 2-3 florets; glumes lanceolate, acute, curved, the first sickle-shaped 1.7-2.5 mm long, 1-nerved, the second 2-3 mm long, 1- or 2-nerved, scaberulous on the keel; lemmas 2.5-3.5 mm long, 5-nerved, sericeous on the keel, sometimes puberulent on the marginal nerves, webbed at base, awnless; palea subequal to the lemma; anthers 1.3-2 mm long.

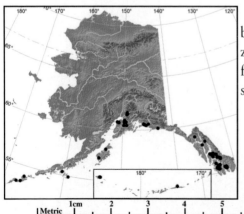

Introduced grass present, but uncommon in moist riparian zones of shaded streams. Escaped from planted lawns and disturbed sites.

Roughstalk bluegrass

Tribe: Poeae

open panicle inflorescence

glumes

lemma

palea

florets

panicle branches

spikelets

prominent
lemma
nerves

ligule

cobwebby
lemma

upper
glume

lower
glume

upper
glume

upper
glume
scabrous
panicle
branches

Glaucous bluegrass

Poa glauca Vahl subsp. *glauca*
Poa glaucantha Gaudin

Perennial, usually densely tufted; usually glaucous colored, wirelike culms, usually rounded, single node at about ⅓ its length; open-panicle inflorescence, several times longer than wide; leaf blades lax and soft, boat tipped; membranous ligule; spikelets relatively small, compressed, not in 1-sided clusters; glumes shorter than the multiple florets within them; glumes and lemmas awnless; lemmas usually webbed at the base, pubescent on the keel, marginal nerves or both, sometimes on the internerves as well, without a distinct nerve between keel and marginal nerve, usually keeled to base, nerves converging toward tip; anthers 1.1 mm or longer.

Plants perennial, tufted; glaucous colored; slender culms wiry, 0.5-7 dm tall, smooth, straight to slightly decumbent; the leaves both basal and cauline, 2-3 mm wide, to 12 cm long; ligules 1-5 mm long.

Panicle 1-16 cm long, open and diffuse; the branches mostly naked at the base; spikelets 3-4 mm long, 3-5 florets, several times longer than wide, laterally compressed; lemmas usually webbed at the base, pubescent on the keel and lateral nerves, awnless; palea keels scabrous, glabrous, or puberulent at the midlength; anthers usually 1.2-2.5 mm long.

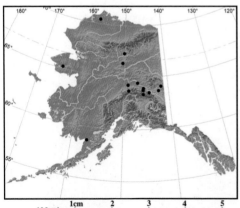

Native grass of high elevation and dry tundra habitats. Present in disturbed rocky areas like roadways. Often confused with *Poa glauca* subsp. *rupicola* and *P. interior*. Commercialized as the cultivar 'Tundra' and used in Interior and Arctic Alaska revegetation projects. May have a wider distribution than shown.

Glaucous bluegrass
Tribe: Poeae

panicle branch

appressed to open panicle

palea

florets

spikelets

ligule

palea

lemma

lemma

callus web

anthers

floret

glumes

Timberline bluegrass

Poa glauca subsp. *rupicola* (Nash) W.A. Weber
Poa rupicola Nash

Perennial, usually densely tufted; usually glaucous colored, wirelike culms, usually round, single node at about ⅓ its length; narrowly lanceoloid panicle inflorescence, several times longer than wide; leaf blades lax and soft, boat tipped; membranous ligule; spikelets relatively small, compressed, not in 1-sided clusters; glumes shorter than the multiple florets within them; glumes and lemmas awnless; lemmas not webbed at the base, hairy nerves, without a distinct nerve between keel and marginal nerve, usually keeled to base, nerves converging toward tip; anthers 1.1 mm or longer.

Plants perennial, tufted; glaucous colored; slender culms wiry, 0.5-1.5 dm tall, smooth, straight to slightly decumbent; the leaves both basal and cauline, 2-3 mm wide, to 12 cm long; ligules 1-5 mm long.

Panicle 1-5 cm long, usually narrowly lanceoloid; the branches mostly naked at the base; spikelets 3-4 mm long, 3- to 5-flowered, several times longer than wide, laterally compressed; lemmas never webbed at the base, at least a few hairs between the veins, awnless; palea keels scabrous, glabrous, or puberulent at the midlength; anthers usually 1.2-2.5 mm long.

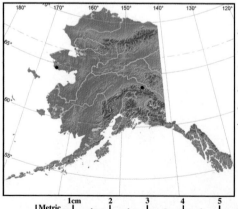

Native grass of dry rocky slopes at high elevations. Subspecies map suggests uncommon in Alaska, but the species, *Poa glauca*, with the exception of the Aleutian Islands is widely distributed across Alaska.

250

Timberline bluegrass
Tribe: Poeae

panicle branch

appressed panicle inflorescence

anthers

palea

lemmas

florets

ligule

spikelet

anthers

hairy nerves of lemmas

glumes

Inland bluegrass
Poa interior Rydb.

Perennial, tufted; narrow to pyramidal-panicle inflorescence, longer than wide, lower branches usually more than 2 per node; culms with 2 nodes, usually rounded; membranous ligule, usually 0.5-1.5 mm long; boat-tipped leaves; spikelets relatively small, 3-6 mm long, compressed; not in 1-sided clusters; glumes shorter than the multiple florets within them; glumes and lemmas awnless; lemmas mostly webbed at the base, sometimes scantly so, pubescent on the keel, marginal nerves or both, sometimes on the internerves as well; anthers 1.1 mm or longer.

Plants perennial, tufted; culms 2-5.1 dm tall, nodes 2, highest node between ⅓-⅔ culm's length; blades 2-10 cm long, 1-2 mm wide, flat, boat tipped; auricles absent; ligules membranous, about 0.5-1.5 mm long, truncate, erose-ciliolate, puberulent abaxially.

Inflorescence a narrow to pyramidal panicle, 5-15 cm long, 2.5-4 times width at maturity; branches erect or ascending; spikelets usually 2- to 3-flowered, 3-6 mm long; glumes shorter than the florets within them, 3-nerved, first glume about 2.2 mm long, keeled; lemmas compressed-keeled, about 2.5 mm long, webbed at base, the web sometimes scant or obscure, silky-villous below on keel and marginal nerves; anthers 1.3-2.5 mm long.

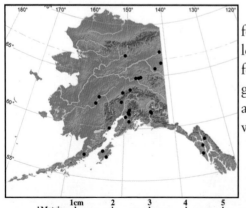

Native grass generally found in dry to mesic habitats of lower to middle elevations. Often found in open forest margins and growing on moss covered rocks and scree. Not known to occur in western or arctic Alaska.

Inland bluegrass
Tribe: Poeae

florets

palea

open panicle inflorescence

lemma

panicle with stiff branches

panicle branch

rachilla

anthers greater than 1 mm

spikelets

lower glume

upper glume

rachis

short ligule

Woodland bluegrass

Poa nemoralis L.

Perennial, densely tufted; narrowly lanceolate to ovoid panicle inflorescence, longer than wide, lower branches usually 2-5 per node; culms with 3-5 nodes, usually rounded; membranous ligule, less than 1 mm long; boat-tipped leaves; spikelets relatively small, 3-8 mm long, compressed, not in 1-sided clusters; glumes shorter than the multiple florets within them; glumes and lemmas awnless; lemmas mostly webbed at the base, sometimes scantly so, pubescent on the keel, marginal nerves or both, internerves glabrous; anthers to 1.9 mm long.

Plants perennial, densely tufted; culms 3-8 dm tall, nodes 3-5, top node ½-¾ culm's length; blades 0.8-3 mm wide, flat, appressed, boat-tipped; auricles absent; ligules membranous, about 0.2-0.8 mm long, truncate, minutely ciliolate.

Inflorescence a narrowly lanceolate to ovoid moderately congested panicle, to 20 cm long, 2.5-4 times width at maturity; branches ascending to spreading; spikelets usually 3-5 florets, 3-8 mm long, glumes shorter than the florets within them; first glume 3-nerved and long tapered to a point, 6.4-11 times longer than wide; lemmas compressed, keeled, about 2.4-4 mm long, webbed at base, the web sometimes scant or obscure, silky-villous below on keel and marginal nerves; anthers 0.8-1.9 mm long.

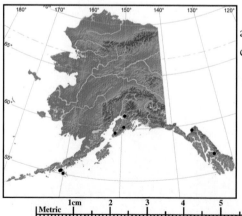

Introduced grass growing at the forest edge or within open canopy areas.

Woodland bluegrass
Tribe: Poeae

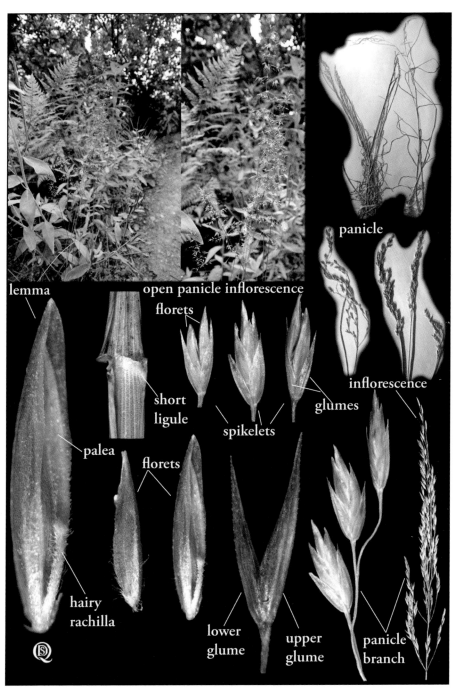

panicle

inflorescence

lemma

open panicle inflorescence

florets

short ligule

spikelets

glumes

palea

florets

hairy rachilla

lower glume

upper glume

panicle branch

Fowl bluegrass

Poa palustris L.

Poa eyerdamii Hultén.

Perennial, loosely tufted; open, lax panicle inflorescence at maturity, lower branches usually 2-9 per node; culms with 3-5 nodes, usually rounded; membranous ligule, 1.5-6 mm long; boat-tipped leaves; spikelets relatively small, 3-5 mm long, compressed, not in 1-sided clusters; glumes shorter than the multiple florets within them; glumes and lemmas awnless; lemmas distinctly webbed at the base, pubescent on the keel, marginal nerves or both, internerves glabrous; anthers 1.1 mm or longer.

Plants perennial, usually loosely tufted; culms 2.5-12 dm tall, may branch at nodes above the base, nodes 3-5, top node at about ½ their length; blades 1.5-8 mm wide, flat, lax, usually several per culm, boat-tipped; auricles absent; ligules membranous, 1.5-6 mm long, obtuse to acute.

Inflorescence an open nodding, lax panicle at maturity, usually 13-30 cm long, branches in rather distinct fascicles, 2-9 per node, naked below, rather congested with 25-100+ spikelets; spikelets 2-5 florets, 3-5 mm long; first glume 2-3 mm long, 1- or obscurely 3-nerved, second glume about 3 mm long, 3-nerved; lemmas 2.5-3 mm long, webbed at the base (rather scant on some), villous on keel and marginal nerves, intermediate nerves rather faint; anthers 1.3-1.8 mm long.

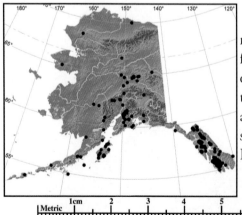

Native grass common to meadow willow thickets, forest margins, and moist banks of streams and rivers. Found throughout Alaska. Considered a contaminant to commercial seed produced in Alaska and the Pacific Northwest.

256

Fowl bluegrass

Tribe: Poeae

open panicle inflorescence

panicle branch

florets

anther

lemma

florets

cobwebby hairs

ligule

spikelet

lower glume

upper glume

spikelet

Dune bluegrass
Poa macrantha Vasey

Perennial, loosely tufted, rhizomatous, stoloniferous, rhizomes and stolons to 4 m long, stout, robust; inflorescence an erect congested compressed panicle, not in 1-sided clusters; culms to 6 dm tall, 1.5-2 mm thick, bases decumbent, usually rounded; membranous ligule, 1-5 mm long; boat-tipped leaves; spikelets 9-17 mm long, compressed; glumes shorter than the multiple florets within them; glumes and lemmas awnless; calluses usually with a crown of hairs; lemma nerve interspaces with long or lanate hairs near the base, nerves converging towards the tip; anthers 1.1 mm or longer.

Plants perennial; usually loosely tufted, rhizomatous and stoloniferous, both stout, robust, and to 4 m long; auricles absent; innovation leaf blades to 30 cm long; ligules membranous, 1-5 mm long.

Panicles 3-15 cm long, erect, contracted, often interrupted, congested with 15-80 spikelets; 1-2 branches per node, erect, stiff with up to 17 spikelets; spikelets 9-17 mm long, 3-6 florets, glumes shorter than the florets within them; glumes compressed; calluses with a crown of hairs; lemmas to 11 mm long, distinctly keeled, keels and veins short-villous to softly puberulent, interspaces may be puberulent near the base; palea glabrous between keel and marginal nerves; vestigial anthers 0.1-0.2 mm long, regular 3-4 mm long.

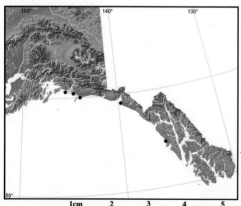

Native grass of coastal sand dunes. In Alaska, it grows from the southeast to the Copper River Delta on the outer exposed coastlines, not on the leeward sides of the archipelago's islands. Now must compete with the introduced *Ammophila arenaria* and other exotic species which have yet to be collected in Alaska.

Dune bluegrass

Tribe: Poeae

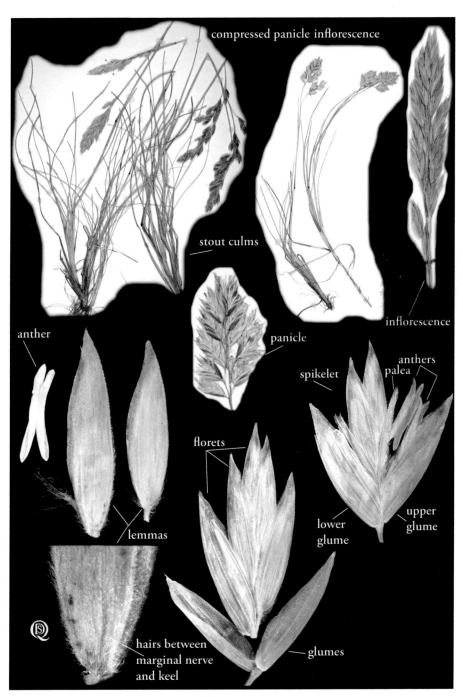

compressed panicle inflorescence

stout culms

inflorescence

anther

panicle

spikelet

anthers
palea

florets

lemmas

lower
glume

upper
glume

hairs between
marginal nerve
and keel

glumes

Cottonball bluegrass

Poa sublanata Reverd.

Perennial, loosely tufted, highly rhizomatous; inflorescence a contracted to narrow open pyramidal panicle, not in 1-sided clusters; culms usually 2-4 dm tall, slender, not stout, usually round, erect or bases decumbent; membranous ligule, boat-tipped leaves; spikelets 4-6.5 mm long, compressed; glumes shorter than the multiple florets within them; glumes and lemmas awnless; lemma area between the keels and marginal nerves completely covered by hairs, keels and marginal nerves densely hairy, cottony appearance, nerves converging towards the tip; palea pubescent between keel and marginal nerves; anthers 1.1 mm or longer.

Plants perennial, very rhizomatous; rhizomes usually thin; culms mostly solitary or a few together, usually 2-4 dm tall, not branching above the base, blades 1-5 mm wide, boat-tipped; ligules 1-6 mm long.

Panicles usually 5-9 cm long, loosely contracted to open, lanceoloid to narrowly pyramidal, sparse with 25-60 spikelets; 2-5 branches per node, 1-3 cm long with 1-5 spikelets per branch; spikelets usually 4-6.5 mm long, laterally compressed with 2-4 florets; glumes to 5 mm long, shorter than the floret within them; calluses dorsally and copiously webbed; lemma veins copiously hairy, cottony, lateral veins prominent, less hairy, awnless; anthers 1.8-2.5 mm long.

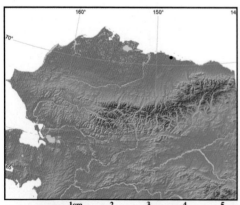

Native grass of dry tundra, disturbances, sand dunes, and other sandy areas near the high arctic coast. Individual culms are usually spread out as this species is highly rhizomatous.

Cottonball bluegrass
Tribe: Poeae

strongly rhizomatous and sand dunes

open panicle inflorescence

cottony hair of the lemmas

florets

spikelets

ligule

glumes

scabrous palea

lemma web

panicle branch

Arctic bluegrass

Poa arctica subsp. *caespitans* Simmons *ex* Nannf.

Perennial, densely to loosely tufted, rhizomes poorly developed, short; inflorescence an open, lax panicle, not in 1-sided clusters; culms to 6 dm tall, slender, not stout, usually round; membranous ligule 2-4 mm long, boat-tipped leaves; spikelets 4.5-8 mm long, compressed; glumes shorter than the multiple florets within them; glumes and lemmas awnless; calluses webbed; lemmas 3-6 mm long, area between the keels and marginal nerves hairy, not dense, sometimes nearly glabrous, nerves converging towards the tip; palea pubescent between keel and marginal nerves; anthers 1.1 mm or longer, generally aborted.

Plants perennial, densely to loosely tufted, rhizomes short; culms mostly solitary or a few together, to 6 dm tall, bases usually decumbent, not branching above the base; leaves folded or flat, boat tipped; ligules 2-4 mm long.

Panicles erect to lax, open; branches ascending to widely spreading, somewhat flexuous, proximal branches ¼-½ the panicle length; spikelets 4.5-8 mm long, compressed; rachilla internodes usually glabrous; calluses webbed; lemmas 3-6 mm long; palea keels glabrous or long-villous; nerves converging towards the tip; palea glabrous between keel and marginal nerves; anthers 1.1 mm long or longer, usually aborted when plants are mature.

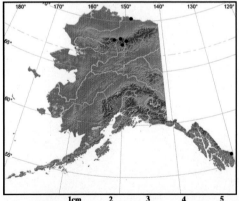

Native grass of the arctic high-elevation wet tundra. Distinguished from other *P. arctica* subspecies only by its more tufted growth form and sterile anthers.

Arctic bluegrass
Tribe: Poeae

panicle branch

open panicle inflorescence

floret

palea

anther

lemma

palea

florets

aborted anthers

glumes

spikelet

ligule

263

Arctic bluegrass

Poa arctica subsp. *lanata* (Scribn. & Merr.) Soreng

Poa lanata Scribn. & Merr.

Perennial, densely to loosely tufted, rhizomes well developed as short subterranean runners; inflorescence an open, lax panicle, not in 1-sided clusters, branches often widely spreading; culms to 6 dm tall, not stout, usually round; membranous ligule 2-4 mm long, boat-tipped leaves; spikelets relatively small, 6-8 mm long, compressed, sometimes bulbiferous; glumes shorter than the multiple florets within them; glumes and lemmas awnless; calluses copiously webbed, glabrous in bulbiferous plants; lemmas 4.5-6 mm long, area between the keels and marginal nerves hairy, not dense, sometimes nearly glabrous, nerves converging towards the tip; rachilla usually hairy; palea pubescent between keel and marginal nerves; anthers 1.1 mm or longer.

Plants perennial, rhizomes subterranean runners; culms solitary or a few together, to 6 dm tall, bases usually decumbent, not branching above the base; leaves folded or flat; ligules 2-4 mm long.

Panicles erect to lax, open; branches ascending to widely spreading, somewhat flexuous, proximal branches $^2/_5$-$^3/_5$ the panicle length; spikelets 6-8 mm long, compressed; rachilla sometimes muriculate, somewhat villous or glabrous; calluses webbed, web copious; lemmas 4.5-6 mm long; palea keels short- to long-villous; anthers usually developed, 1.4-2.5 mm long.

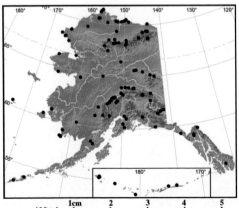

Native grass common to mountains of Alaska. Appears to be prevalent on alpine dry rocky ridges and in dry disturbed areas of tundra. Often viviparous.

Arctic bluegrass
Tribe: Poeae

open and lax panicle inflorescence

panicle branches

spikelets

florets

glumes

lemma webs

viviperous / bulbiferous plant

spikelet

branch

anthers

ligule

hairy rachilla

Arctic bluegrass

Poa arctica R. Br. subsp. *arctica*
P. arctica subsp. *longiculmis* Hultén
P. arctica subsp. *williamsii* (Nash) Hultén

Perennial, usually loosely tufted, rhizomes well developed as subterranean runners; inflorescence an open, lax panicle, not in 1-sided clusters, branches often widely spreading; culms to 6 dm tall, not stout, usually round; membranous ligule 2-4 mm long, boat-tipped leaves; spikelets 4.5-6 mm long, compressed, sometimes bulbiferous; glumes shorter than the multiple florets within them; glumes and lemmas awnless; copiously webbed calluses, glabrous in bulbiferous plants; lemmas 3-4.5 mm long, area between the keels and marginal nerves hairy, not dense, may be nearly glabrous; rachilla usually glabrous; palea pubescent between keel and marginal nerves; anthers 1.1 mm or longer.

Plants perennial, rhizomes well developed; culms mostly solitary or a few together, to 6 dm tall, bases usually decumbent, not branching above the base; leaves 1-6 mm wide, folded or flat, boat tipped; ligules 2-4 mm long, obtuse to acute.

Panicles erect to lax, open; branches ascending to widely spreading, somewhat flexuous, proximal branches $^2/_5$-$^3/_5$ the panicle length; spikelets 4.5-6 mm long, compressed; rachilla usually glabrous; calluses sparsely to copiously webbed; lemmas 3-4.5 mm long; palea keels puberulent to long-villous; anthers usually developed, 1.4-2.5 mm long.

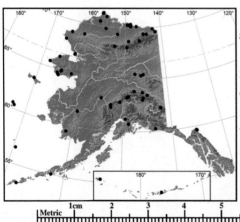

Native grass common across Alaska's tundra and subalpine/alpine regions. Often found where natural or manmade disturbances occur and where mineral soil is exposed. The viviparous or bulbiferous form may also be present.

Arctic bluegrass
Tribe: Poeae

spikelets of a panicle branch

rachilla

open lax panicle inflorescence

viviparous plant

palea

florets

florets with less hair between nerves

lemma

spikelet

glumes

ligule

bulbiferous form

267

Porsild's bluegrass

Poa porsildii Gjaerev.

Perennial, densely tufted, not stoloniferous or rhizomatous; dioecious; inflorescence an open, erect or nodding pyramidal panicle, sparse with fewer than 20 spikelets, 2-6 cm long, not in 1-sided clusters, 1-2 branches per node; culms usually round; membranous ligule, boat-tipped leaves; spikelets relatively small, 4-7 mm long, compressed; glumes shorter than the multiple florets within them; glumes and lemmas awnless; calluses not webbed, glabrous; lemmas 4-6 mm long, glabrous, usually keeled to base, nerves converging towards the tip; anthers 1.1 mm or longer.

Plants perennial, densely tufted, no rhizomes or stolons; culms usually 1.7-3 dm tall, erect or bases decumbent, 1-2 exserted nodes; innovation leaf blades not or indistinctly differentiated from the cauline blades, flat or weakly involute; leaves 1-3 mm wide; ligules 1-2 mm long.

Panicles an open, erect or nodding pyramidal panicle, sparse, with fewer than 20 spikelets; branches 2-4 cm long, ascending to widely spreading with 1-3 spikelets; spikelets 4-7 mm long, compressed, 3-4 florets; rachilla internodes glabrous or sparsely puberulent; glumes shorter than the florets within them; calluses glabrous; lemmas 4-6 mm long, sparsely to moderately densely scabrous, usually glabrous; palea keels sparsely to moderately densely scabrous; vestigial anthers 0.1-0.2 mm long, regular 2.5-3 mm long.

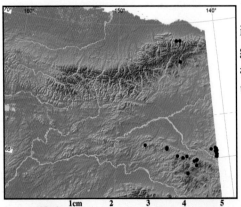

Native grass of the interior alpine. This dioecious grass occupies turf type tundra and heath habitat above interior treeline.

Porsild's bluegrass
Tribe: Poeae

R.J. Soreng

R.J. Soreng

R.J. Soreng

R.J. Soreng

open to contracted panicle inflorescence
with few spikelets

stigma

palea

lemma

scabrous lemmas

ligule

ligule

panicle
branches

florets

palea

florets

lemma

thin glumes

spikelets

Alpine bluegrass

Poa alpina L.

Perennial, tufted; open-panicle inflorescence, about as wide as long; spikelets not in 1-sided clusters, culm usually round; leaf blades mostly basal, lax, relatively wide and short, soft, boat-tipped; membranous ligule; spikelets relatively small, broad, compressed, glumes shorter than the multiple florets within them; glumes and lemmas awnless; lemmas not webbed at the base, strongly villous on both the keel, marginal nerves or both, sometimes on the internerves as well, usually keeled to base, nerves converging towards the tip; anthers 1.1 mm or longer.

Plants perennial, tufted; culms 1-4 dm tall; leaf blades short, 2-10 mm wide, flat or folded, boat tipped; ligules membranous, to 5 mm long, truncate or shortly acuminate, entire.

Panicle 2-8 cm long, ovoid to short-pyramidal, about as wide as long, lower branches often reflexed; spikelets to 6.2 mm long, 3-5 florets, broad, purple or purplish; glumes broad, abruptly acute, first glume 3 mm long, second glume somewhat longer; lemmas broad, compressed-keeled, 3-4 mm long, callus not webbed, strongly villous on both keel and marginal nerves, also pubescent on internerves below, the intermediate nerves faint; anthers 1.3-2.3 mm long.

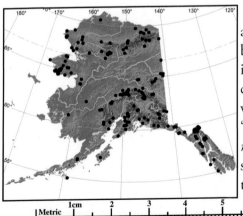

Native grass of subalpine and alpine meadows. Colonizes bare mineral soil and is common in disturbed riparian areas. Alaska's cultivar 'Gruening' has been widely used for revegetation. 'Gruening' and *Lolium multiflorum* are allelopathic and should not be planted together in the same seed mix.

Alpine bluegrass
Tribe: Poeae

broad and short basal leaves

panicle as wide as long

open panicle inflorescence

palea

florets

anther

branch and spikelets

lemma hairy on keel

callus glabrous

glumes

ligule

flat leaf blades

spikelets strongly compressed

271

Alaska bluegrass

Poa paucispicula Scribn. & Merr.

Poa merrilliana Hitchc.

Perennial, loosely tufted; spreading-panicle inflorescence, longer than wide, 2.5-10 cm long, few branches; lower branches usually 1-2 per node; culms to 3 dm tall, usually round; membranous ligule; boat-tipped leaves; spikelets relatively small, ovate, 4-6 mm long, compressed, not in 1-sided clusters, glumes shorter than the multiple florets within them; glumes and lemmas awnless; lemmas webbed at the base, short- to long-villous on the keel, marginal nerves or both, sometimes on the internerves as well, usually keeled to base, nerves converging towards the tip; anthers less than 1.1 mm.

Plants perennial, loosely tufted; culms to 3 dm tall; leaf blades 1-3 mm wide, flat or folded, boat tipped; auricles absent; ligules membranous, 1-2 mm long, truncate to obtuse.

Panicle 2.5-10 cm long, lax, to almost erect, open, sparse, 1-2 branches per node, branches often reflexed, smooth, with 1-5 spikelets; spikelets 4-6 mm long, 3-5 florets; glumes shorter than the florets within them; calluses sparsely webbed; lemmas 3-4 mm long, usually purple, awnless, keels and marginal veins short- to long-villous; anthers 0.4-1 mm long.

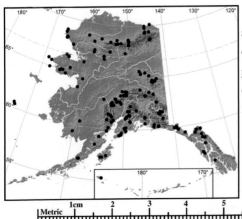

Native grass of alpine and subalpine zones throughout most of Alaska. Rather common and grows on rocky mesic areas. Often overlooked as it is delicate with few spreading branches.

Alaska bluegrass
Tribe: Poeae

open panicle inflorescence

florets

ligule

spikelets deep purple

glumes

anther

spikelets

lemmas

callus web

panicle branch

R. J. Soreng

Bog bluegrass
Poa leptocoma Trin.

Perennial, tufted; spreading-panicle inflorescence, longer than wide, 5-15 cm long, few branches; branches usually 1-3 per node; culms 1.5-10 dm tall, usually round; membranous ligule; boat-tipped leaves; spikelets relatively small, 4-8 mm long, compressed, not in 1-sided clusters; glumes shorter than multiple florets within them; glumes and lemmas awnless; calluses sparsely webbed, lemmas 3-4 mm long, pubescent on the keel, marginal nerves or both, sometimes on the internerves as well, usually keeled to base, nerves converging towards the tip; anthers less than 1.1 mm.

Plants perennial, tufted; culms 1.5-10 dm tall; leaf blades 1-4 mm wide, 4-10 cm long, flat or folded, boat tipped; auricles absent; ligules membranous, 1.5-4 mm long, obtuse to acute.

Inflorescence a nodding, few-flowered panicle, 5-15 cm long, branches capillary, ascending to spreading, subflexuous, the lower usually in 2's; spikelets narrow, 4-8 mm long, 2-5 florets, laterally compressed; glumes shorter than the florets within them; calluses sparsely webbed at the base; lemmas compressed-keeled, 3-4 mm long, narrow to acuminate, pubescent on the keel and marginal nerves or sometimes nearly glabrous; anthers 0.2-1.1 mm long.

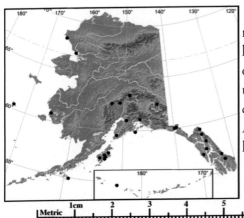

Native grass generally restricted to very wet meadows, lakeshores, and bogs usually near or below timberline. Rather uncommon in Alaska and may be confused with the more prevalent *P. paucispicula*, but *P. leptocoma*'s lower branches are scabrous.

Bog bluegrass
Tribe: Poeae

open to nodding panicle inflorescence

palea lemma

anthers

florets

panicle branch

ligule

web of hairs

spikelets

anthers 0.2-1.1 mm long

unequal glumes

Short-flowered bluegrass

Poa pseudoabbreviata Roshev.
Poa brachyanthera Hultén

Perennial, densely tufted, mostly glaucous; delicate and spreading-panicle inflorescence, 2-7 cm long, as wide as long, erect, sparse; branches usually 1-3 per node, long and slender; culms usually 0.4-2 dm tall, usually round; membranous ligule; boat-tipped leaves; spikelets relatively small, 3-5 mm long, laterally compressed, not in 1-sided clusters; glumes shorter than multiple florets within them; glumes and lemmas awnless; calluses glabrous, lemmas 2-3 mm long, keel and marginal nerves crispy puberulent, intercostal regions glabrous, usually keeled to base, nerves converging towards the tip; anthers less than 1.1 mm long.

Plants perennial, densely tufted, no rhizomes or stolons; culms usually 0.4-2 dm tall; leaf blades 0.5-1 mm wide, flat or folded, thin, soft, boat tipped; auricles absent; ligules membranous, 1-4 mm long.

Panicles 2-7 cm long, widths equal to lengths, broadly rhomboidal to pyramidal, open, sparse; branches 1.5-5 cm long ascending to spreading, divaricate, slender; spikelets 3-5 mm long laterally compressed, 2-4 florets, glumes shorter than the florets within them; lemmas 2-3 mm long, keeled, keels and marginal veins crisply puberulent, intercostal regions glabrous, apices acute; paleas scabrous over the keels; anthers 0.2-0.7 mm long.

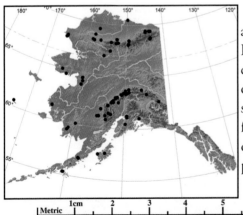

Native grass of the alpine and dry tundra areas of Alaska. Found in disturbed areas like frost cracks, hummocks, rocky slopes, dry ridges, and open areas below snowbanks. May be distinguished from other alpine species by its delicate, long, and spreading panicle branches.

Short-flowered bluegrass
Tribe: Poeae

florets

anthocyanic spikelets

open and lax panicle

R.J. Soreng

R.J. Soreng

branches 1.5-5 cm long

glumes

mostly glabrous florets

rachilla internodes less than 1 mm long

callus not webbed

anthers less than 1.1 mm long

Dwarf bluegrass
Poa abbreviata R.Br. subsp. *abbreviata*

Perennial, densely tufted; narrow-panicle inflorescence, longer than wide, congested, lower panicle branches 1-3 per node; culms 0.5-1.5 dm tall, not much longer than the blades, usually rounded; blades 5-10 cm long, lax, and soft, boat tipped; membranous ligule; spikelets relatively small, laterally compressed, not in 1-sided clusters; glumes shorter than the multiple florets within them; glumes and lemmas awnless; callus usually not webbed; lemmas short- to long-villous on the keel, marginal nerves or both, softly puberulent to short-villous on intercostal regions; anthers less than 1.1 mm long.

Plants perennial, tufted; culms 0.5-1.5 dm tall; blades about 1 mm wide, 5-10 cm long, folded, boat tipped; auricles absent; ligules membranous, usually 0.4-1.7 mm long, milky white to hyaline; truncate to acute.

Inflorescence a narrow, condensed panicle, 1.5-5 cm long, contracted, congested; spikelets 4-6.5 mm long, laterally compressed, 2-4 florets; glumes shorter than the florets within them; lemmas compressed-keeled, 2.5-5.8 mm long, webless or sometimes sparsely webbed on the callus, pubescent on the keel and marginal nerves, short-pubescent on the intercostal regions; anthers 0.2-0.8 mm long.

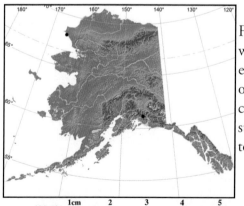

Native grass of the alpine. Found in disturbed rocky areas where it is exposed to the elements and not competing with other grasslike plants. Few collections identified to this subspecies. Species range similar to *P. abbreviata* subsp. *pattersonii*.

278

Dwarf bluegrass
Tribe: Poeae

spikelets

compressed panicle
with short branches

bisexual
spikelets

florets

glumes

caryopsis

glumes

panicles

florets

florets

ligule

Patterson's bluegrass

Poa abbreviata subsp. *pattersonii* (Vasey) Á Löve,
D. Löve & B.M. Kapoor; *Poa pattersonii* Vasey

Perennial, densely tufted; narrow-panicle inflorescence, longer than wide, congested, lower panicle branches 1-3 per node; culms 0.5-1.5 dm tall, not much longer than the blades, usually rounded; blades 5-10 cm long, lax, and soft, boat tipped; membranous ligule; spikelets relatively small, laterally compressed, not in 1-sided clusters; glumes shorter than the multiple florets within them; glumes and lemmas awnless; callus usually webbed; lemmas short- to long-villous on the keel, marginal nerves or both, glabrous to softly puberulent on intercostal regions; anthers usually less than 1.1 mm long.

Plants perennial, tufted; culms 0.5-1.5 dm tall; blades about 1 mm wide, 5-10 cm long, folded, boat tipped; auricles absent; ligules membranous, usually 0.8-5.5 mm long, milky white to hyaline, obtuse to acute.

Inflorescence a narrow, condensed panicle, 1.5-5 cm long, contracted, congested; spikelets 4-6.5 mm long, laterally compressed, 2- to 4-flowered; glumes shorter than the florets within them; lemmas compressed-keeled, 2.5-5.8 mm long, usually webbed at the callus, long villous on the keel and marginal nerves, glabrous to softly puberulent on the intercostal regions; anthers 0.6-1.2 mm long.

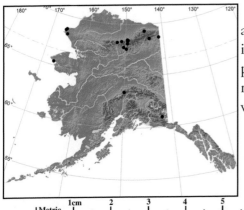

Native grass of alpine dry and rocky hillsides. Mostly found in the Brooks Range but is likely present in all other mountain ranges. Does not compete well with other grasslike plants.

280

Patterson's bluegrass

Tribe: Poeae

compressed panicle inflorescence
spikelets
anthers
glabrous
to webbed
callus
caryopsis
glumes
glumes
short
branches
plants
ligule
florets
lemma
hairy
keel
palea
hairy
marginal nerve
webbed
callus
glumes
glabrous
callus
R. J. Soreng

Common brookgrass
Catabrosa aquatica (L.) P. Beauv.

Perennial, rhizomatous, stoloniferous when growing in water; open-panicle inflorescence; membranous ligule; glumes shorter than the 1 or usually 2 fertile florets within them, not papery, usually definitely keeled; lemmas soft and nerves parallel, not converging toward the tip.

Plants perennial, rhizomatous, sometimes stoloniferous; culms 1-6 dm tall, glabrous; sheaths closed, auricles absent; ligules membranous, 1-8 mm long; leaf blades to 20 cm long, 13 mm wide, flat.

Panicle to 35 cm long, 12 cm wide, erect, oblong or pyramidal, the branches spreading in somewhat distant whorls; spikelets about 1.5-3.5 mm long, usually 2-flowered, rarely 1-flowered; first glume to 1.3 mm long, second glume to 2.2 mm long, both truncate, scarious and often toothed at apex; lemmas 2-3 mm long, 3-nerved, the nerves parallel and prominent, brownish, glabrous, with broad apex, scarious, often erose; rachilla joint usually at least 1 mm long; anthers 2-3 mm long.

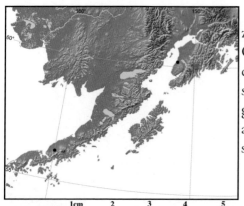

Native grass of wet riparian zones along streams and springs. Generally growing in water and a colonizer of newly deposited sediment. Rare in Alaska and generally replaced by more aggressive riparian grasses and tall sedges.

Common brookgrass
Tribe: Poeae

brookgrass habitat

spikelets

stolons

florets

palea

loose panicle inflorescence

rachilla

lemma

lower glume

upper glume

2 or 3 floret spikelet

ligule

Pendant grass
Arctophila fulva (Trin.) Andersson

Perennial, rhizomatous, to 10 dm tall; open-panicle inflorescence, branches mostly erect to pendulous; ligule membranous; aerial sheaths closed over 1/2 their length; leaves not boat-tipped, usually 1-5 mm wide; spikelets to 8 mm long, usually 2-7 florets; glumes blunt, awnless; shorter than the multiple florets within them; disarticulation of florets above the glumes; lemmas with parallel nerves, not papery, awnless, apices obtuse; anthers 1.2-3 mm long.

Plants perennial, rhizomatous; culms 1-10 dm tall, erect, often rooting at the lower nodes; sheaths of aquatic leaves closed to their apices, sheaths of aerial leaves closed over ½ their length; auricles absent; blades to 23 cm long, 1-5 mm wide; ligules membranous, usually 2-8 mm long.

Panicles to 20 cm long, 11 cm wide, open; spikelets to 8 mm long, usually 2-7 florets; glumes to 5 mm long, lower glumes exceeded by the lowest floret, upper glumes shorter than to longer than the lowest floret, not papery; lemmas 2.5-4 mm long, nerves parallel and not converging at the tip.

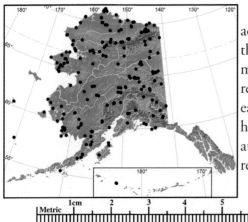

Native grass of wet to aquatic habitat. Common around the edges of lakes, ponds and slow moving streams. Assumes a very red color during late summer and early fall. Provides important habitat for waterfowl. Some attempts to use *A. fulva* for reclamation have occurred.

Pendant grass
Tribe: Poeae

open and drooping panicle inflorescence

florets

branch

stamens

spikelets

ligule

stigma

rachilla

anthers

lemma nerves
not excurrent

glabrous
ovary

lemma

lowest
floret

palea

upper
glume

lower
glume

upper
glume

285

Common rivergrass
Scolochloa festucacea (Willd.) Link

Perennial, rhizomatous; culms stout; open-panicle inflorescence; membranous ligule to 8 mm long; sheaths open; spikelets rounded on the back; both glumes shorter than the multiple florets within them, papery, disarticulation of the florets is above the glumes; lemma veins parallel, excurrent, not awned, often folded together to form a rudiment near the spikelet summit; callus long pilose.

Plants perennial, strongly rhizomatous, rhizomes succulent; culms to 20 dm tall, stout, to 8 mm thick at the base; sheaths open, blades to 45 cm long, 12 mm wide, flat; auricles absent; ligules membranous, to 8 mm long, acute, lacerate.

Panicles open, 5-30 cm long, loose, the distant branches fascicled, naked below, lowermost as long as panicle; spikelets about to 11 mm long, 3-4 florets, florets approximate, disarticulating above the glumes; glumes nearly equal, the 1st shorter than the adjacent lemma, the 2nd about equal to the distant floret; lemmas firm, to 9 mm long, rounded on back, villous on the callus, 7-nerved, nerves rather faint, excurrent; palea narrow, flat, about as long as lemma; anthers 2-4 mm long.

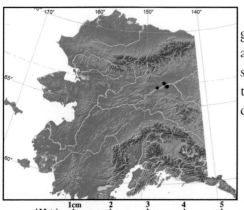

Native riparian grass that grows within ponds, bogs, marshes, and shallow margins of lakes and slow moving streams. Mostly in the Midwest and appears to be a disjunct population in Alaska.

Common rivergrass
Tribe: Poeae

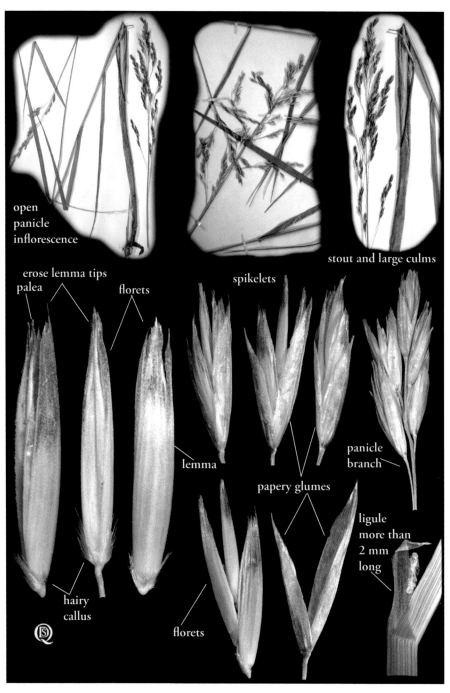

open panicle inflorescence

stout and large culms

erose lemma tips
palea

florets

spikelets

lemma

florets

papery glumes

panicle branch

ligule more than 2 mm long

hairy callus

Weak alkaligrass; Weak mannagrass

Torreyochloa pallida var. *pauciflora* (J. Presl) J.I. Davis
Puccinellia pauciflora (J. Presl) Munz; *Glyceria pauciflora* J. Presl

Perennial, rhizomatous; culms stout; open-panicle inflorescence; membranous ligule; sheaths open; spikelets rounded on the back; glumes not papery, upper glume 3-nerved, both shorter than the multiple florets within them, disarticulation of the florets above the glumes; lemma veins parallel, prominent, not excurrent, awnless.

Plants perennial, rhizomatous; culms to 14.5 dm tall, to 4.8 mm thick at the base, usually erect; sheaths open, cauline blades to 18 mm wide, flat; auricles absent; ligules membranous, to 9 mm long, obtuse to acute.

Panicle open or rather dense, terminal, nodding, to 25 cm long, 1.2-7.7 times as long as wide, rather flexuous, the spikelets crowded on the upper half; spikelets mostly 4-8 florets, 2.2-3.3 mm long, often purplish; glumes broadly ovate or oval, about 1-1.5 mm long; lemmas oblong, 2-2.5 mm long, 5-9 prominent parallel nerves, tip rounded, scarious, somewhat erose; anthers of the lowest floret 0.5-0.7 mm long.

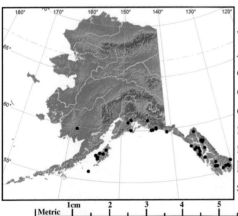

Native grass found in the wet area of riparian zones. Appears to be a colonizer of disturbed areas thus it may be crowded out by tall sedges and other riparian grasses. Usually found in disturbed small slow flowing streams, bogs, and lakeshores. Mostly found in the southern coasts of Alaska.

Weak alkaligrass; Weak mannagrass

Tribe: Poeae

open panicle inflorescence

wet bog habitat

panicle branch

inflorescence

ligule

florets

uneven glumes

spikelets

anthers 0.5-0.7 mm long

florets

palea

lemma

glumes

Goose grass
Puccinellia phryganodes (Trin.) Scribn. & Merr.

Perennial, strongly stoloniferous, not rhizomatous, mat forming within saline coastal sites; diffuse-panicle inflorescence when present, often absent; membranous ligule, to 3 mm long; sheaths open; spikelets rounded on the back; glumes not papery, shorter than the multiple florets within them, upper glume 3-nerved, disarticulation of the florets above the glumes; lemma veins parallel, usually faint, not excurrent, awnless.

Plants perennial, strongly stoloniferous, often forming low mats; culms 0.2-1.5 dm tall, erect to decumbent; leaf blades 0.4-2.2 mm wide; auricles absent; ligules 0.4-1.5 mm long.

Panicles usually not developed, when present, diffuse, lower branches ascending, spikelets confined to the distal ⅓; spikelets to 9 mm long, usually 3-6 florets; glumes rounded to slightly keeled, shorter than the florets within them, not papery; calluses glabrous or almost so; lemmas to 4.5 mm long, rounded, apical margins whitish, hyaline, smooth, entire; palea veins glabrous; anthers 2-2.5 mm long.

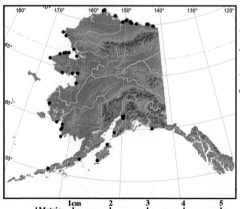

Native grass confined to the coastal high tidelines, in wet, saline meadows, or brackish marshes. Widespread and common in its habitat.

Goose grass
Tribe: Poeae

stoloniferous plant
and forming low mats
on mud flats near the ocean

lemmas

palea

anther

spikelet
florets

panicle

rachilla

glumes

ligule

Tall alkali grass
Puccinellia angustata (R. Br.) E.L. Rand & Redfield

Perennial, tufted, not rhizomatous or mat forming; culms 1-3.5 dm tall; contracted-panicle inflorescence; membranous ligule, to 3 mm long; sheaths open; spikelets rounded on the back, pedicels scabrous; glumes not papery, shorter than the multiple florets within them, upper glume 3-nerved, disarticulation of the florets above the glumes; lemma veins parallel, usually faint, not excurrent, awnless; palea veins with curly, intertwined hairs near the base.

Plants perennial, tufted, not mat forming; culms 1-3.5 dm tall, erect to decumbent; leaf blades usually involute, sometimes flat, 0.5-3 mm wide; auricles absent; ligules 1-3 mm long.

Panicles contracted, sometimes open when mature, to 13 cm long, usually 2-3 branches per lower nodes, spikelets confined to the distal ½ pedicels scabrous; spikelets to 10 mm long with 3-5 florets; glumes rounded on the back, veins obscure, shorter than the florets within them, not papery; calluses with a few hairs; lemmas to 5.2 mm long, rounded, apical margins scabrous, veins parallel, awnless; palea veins with curly intertwined hairs proximally, scabrous distally; anthers usually 0.8-1.1 mm long.

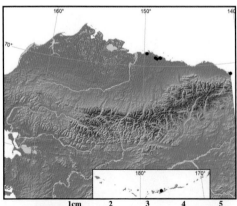

Native grass growing in saline disturbed silty or sandy sediments. Grows above the influence of high tide.

Tall alkali grass
Tribe: Poeae

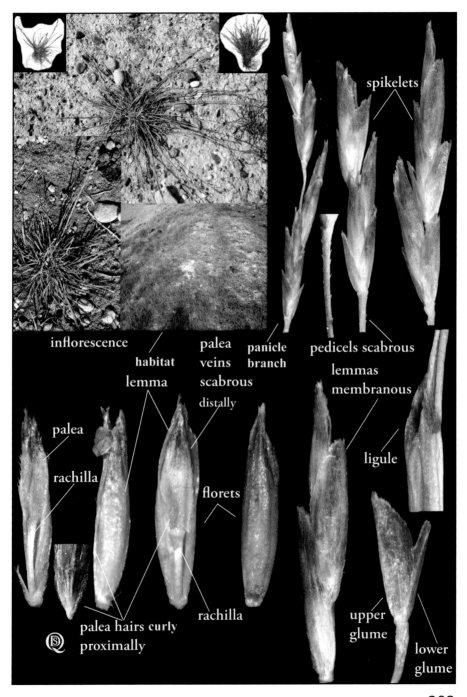

inflorescence

habitat

lemma

palea

rachilla

palea veins scabrous distally

panicle branch

florets

palea hairs curly proximally

rachilla

spikelets

pedicels scabrous

lemmas membranous

ligule

upper glume

lower glume

Vahl's alkali grass

Puccinellia vahliana (Liebm.) Scribn. & Merr.
Colpodium vahlianum (Liebm.) Nevski

Perennial, tufted, not rhizomatous or mat forming, culms 0.5-1.5 dm tall; contracted and dense panicle inflorescence; membranous ligule, to 3 mm long; sheaths open; spikelets rounded on the back, pedicels smooth; glumes not papery, shorter than the multiple florets within them, upper glume 3-nerved, disarticulation of the florets above the glumes; lemma veins parallel, usually faint, not excurrent, awnless; palea veins with curly, intertwined hairs near the base.

Plants perennial, tufted, not mat forming, not rhizomatous; culms 0.5-1.5 dm tall, erect; leaf blades to 8 mm wide, flat or folded; auricles absent; ligules 1-2.5 mm long.

Panicle usually contracted and dense, may be somewhat diffuse at maturity, to 4 cm long, lowest node usually with long and short branches, spikelets usually confined to the distal ⅔; pedicels glabrous and smooth; spikelets to 6.5 mm long with usually 2-4 florets; glumes rounded on the back, veins obscure, shorter than the florets within them, not papery; calluses with a few hairs; lemmas to 5.2 mm long, rounded, apical margins smooth, veins parallel, awnless; palea veins with curly intertwined hairs proximally, scabrous distally; anthers usually 0.8-1.5 mm long.

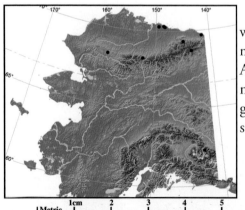

Native grass found in wet or moist gravel, sand, clay, or moss areas of poorly drained soils. Appears to be a colonizer of nonsaline conditions including glacial ephemeral streams, ponds, snowbeds, and springs.

294

Vahl's alkali grass
Tribe: Poeae

smooth
pedicle
anthers
0.8 - 1.5 mm

ligules

floret

palea veins with
curly intertwined
hairs proximally

lemma

spikelets

florets

glumes
over middle
of lowest lemma

R.J. Soreng

295

Wright's alkali grass

Puccinellia wrightii (Scribn. & Merr.) Tzvelev

Colpodium wrightii Scribn. & Merr.

Perennial, tufted, not rhizomatous or mat forming, culms 1.5-4 dm tall; open-diffuse panicle inflorescence; membranous ligule, to 3 mm long; sheaths open; spikelets rounded on the back, pedicels smooth; glumes not papery, shorter than the multiple florets within them, upper glume 3-nerved, disarticulation of the florets above the glumes; lemma veins parallel, usually faint, not excurrent, awnless; palea veins with curly, intertwined hairs near the base.

Plants perennial, tufted, not mat forming, not rhizomatous; culms 1.5-4 dm tall, erect; leaf blades to 8 mm wide, flat or folded; auricles absent; ligules 1-3 mm long.

Panicle open and diffuse at maturity, to 8 cm long, lowest node usually with long branches, spikelets usually confined to the distal ⅓; pedicels glabrous and smooth; spikelets to 7 mm long with usually 4-5 florets; glumes rounded on the back, veins obscure, shorter than the florets within them, not papery; calluses with a few hairs; lemmas to 5 mm long, rounded, apical margins smooth, veins parallel, awnless; palea veins with curly intertwined hairs proximally, scabrous distally; anthers usually 1.5-2.5 mm long.

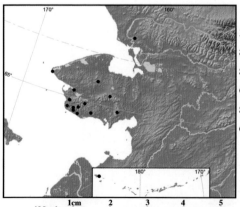

Native grass found in nonsaline conditions on wet aggraded gravel bars within streams and their banks. A rather distinct but uncommon grass similar in appearance to the very common *P. nuttaliana.*

Wright's alkali grass
Tribe: Poeae

smooth pedicels

panicle branch

lemma

palea

open panicle inflorescence

hairy palea veins

palea

lemma

florets

large anthers

stigma

spikelet

ligule

glumes

rachilla

Tundra alkali grass

Puccinellia tenella (Lange) Holmb. *ex* Porsild

Puccinellia langeana (Berlin) T.J. Sørensen

Perennial, tufted, not rhizomatous or mat forming, culms 0.3-1.6 dm tall; contracted, sometimes diffuse panicle inflorescence; membranous ligule, to 3 mm long; sheaths open; spikelets mostly rounded on the back, pedicels smooth; glumes not papery, shorter than the multiple florets within them, upper glume 3-nerved, disarticulation of the florets above the glumes; lemmas 2-2.5 mm long, rounded, veins parallel, usually faint, not excurrent, margins smooth, purple with whitish margins, awnless; palea veins glabrous near the base.

Plants perennial, tufted, not mat forming, not rhizomatous; culms 0.3-1.6 dm tall, erect; leaf blades mostly involute 0.4-0.7 mm in diameter, occasionally flat, 0.5-1.5 mm wide when flat; auricles absent; ligules 0.5-1.7 mm long.

Panicle contracted, sometimes diffuse at maturity, to 5.5 cm long, lower branches erect or ascending, spikelets usually confined to the distal 1/2; pedicels smooth; spikelets to 7 mm long with usually 3-6 florets; glumes rounded on the back, veins distinct, shorter than the florets within them, not papery; calluses with a few hairs; lemmas to 2.5 mm long, rounded, purple with whitish margins, apical margins smooth, veins parallel, awnless; palea veins smooth, glabrous; anthers usually 0.6-0.9 mm long.

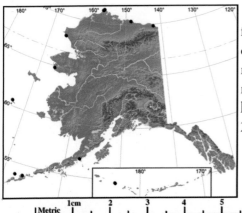

Native low-growing grass found just above the high tideline on coastal sandy spits, salt marshes, silty soils, and among rocks to about 30 feet above sea level. Red stolons in photo (page 299) are those of *Potentilla sp.*

Tundra alkali grass

Tribe: Poeae

anthers · palea · florets · white border on lemmas · caryopsis · lemmas · palea · ligule · rachilla · glumes · panicle

Smooth alkali grass

Puccinellia pumila (Vasey) Hitchc.

P. langeana subsp. *alaskana* (Scribn. & Merr.) T.J. Sørensen *ex* Hultén

Perennial, tufted, sometimes rhizomatous or stoloniferous, not mat forming, culms 0.8-4 dm tall; contracted or diffuse panicle inflorescence; membranous ligule, to 3 mm long; sheaths open; spikelets mostly rounded on the back, pedicels smooth; glumes not papery, shorter than the multiple florets within them, upper glume 3-nerved, disarticulation of the florets above the glumes; lemmas 2.4-4.6 mm long, glabrous, rounded, veins parallel, faint to distinct, not excurrent, margins smooth, somewhat purple, margins not white, awnless; palea veins glabrous near the base.

Plants perennial, tufted, often rhizomatous or stoloniferous when rooting from the lower nodes after being partially buried in sand, not mat forming; culms 0.8-4 dm tall, erect to decumbent; leaf blades 1-3 mm wide, flat to involute; auricles absent; ligules 0.8-2.5 mm long.

Panicle contracted to diffuse, to 20 cm long, lower branches erect or ascending, spikelets from near the bases or confined to the distal ⅔; pedicels smooth; spikelets to 9 mm long, 3-7 florets; glumes rounded on the back, veins obscure or distinct, shorter than the florets within them, not papery; calluses glabrous with a few hairs; lemmas to 4.6 mm long, glabrous, rounded, apical margins smooth, not white, veins parallel, awnless; palea veins smooth, glabrous; anthers usually 0.5-1.2 mm long.

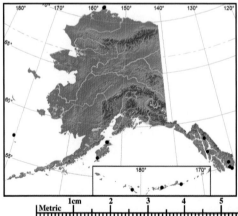

Native grass of sandy areas and among rocks in protected intertidal environments of coastal areas.

Smooth alkali grass
Tribe: Poeae

distinct veins of lemmas

spikelets

inflorescence

glumes

florets

panicle branch

lemma

palea

ligule

anthers

rachilla

unequal glumes

Arctic alkali grass

Puccinellia arctica (Hook.) Fernald & Weath.
Puccinellia agrostidea T.J. Sørensen

Perennial, tufted, not mat forming, culms 1-4 dm tall, erect; contracted or diffuse panicle inflorescence, branches usually more than 2 at the lower nodes; membranous ligule, to 3 mm long; sheaths open; spikelets mostly rounded on the back, pedicels scabrous; glumes not papery, shorter than the multiple florets within them, upper glume 3-nerved, disarticulation of the florets above the glumes; lemmas 2.5-3.7 mm long, somewhat hairy on the lower part, rounded, veins parallel, usually faint, not excurrent, margins smooth or scabrous, not white, awnless; palea veins glabrous near the base.

Plants perennial, tufted, not mat forming; culms 1-4 dm tall, erect; leaf blades usually 0.5-2.2 mm wide, flat, sometimes involute; auricles absent; ligules 0.9-3 mm long.

Panicles contracted to diffuse, lowest nodes with 3-5 branches, branches ascending to horizontal, spikelets usually confined to the distal ⅔; pedicels scabrous; spikelets to 9.5 mm long with usually 3-6 florets; glumes rounded on the back, veins obscure or distinct; calluses glabrous with a few hairs; lemmas 2.5-3.7 mm long, hairy on the bases of the veins, veins parallel, apical margins smooth, not white, often inrolled, parallel, awnless; palea veins glabrous, smooth proximally, sometimes scabrous from midlength to apices; anthers 1.2-2.2 mm long.

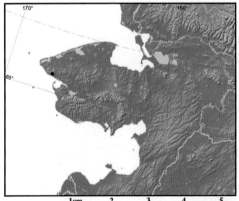

Native grass growing on saline silt, clay, and sandy coastal substrates.

302

Arctic alkali grass

Tribe: Poeae

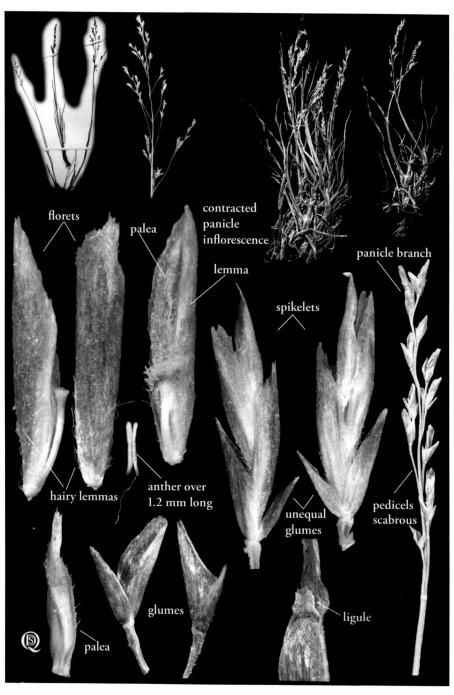

florets

palea

contracted panicle inflorescence

lemma

panicle branch

spikelets

hairy lemmas

anther over 1.2 mm long

unequal glumes

pedicels scabrous

palea

glumes

ligule

303

Anderson's alkali grass

Puccinellia andersonii Swallen

Perennial, tufted, not mat forming, culms 1-2.5 dm tall, usually decumbent, often with unhealthy appearance; contracted or diffuse-panicle inflorescence, branches usually 2 at the lower nodes; membranous ligule, to 3 mm long; sheaths open; spikelets mostly rounded on the back, pedicels smooth or scabrous; glumes not papery, shorter than the multiple florets within them, upper glume 3-nerved, disarticulation of the florets above the glumes; lemmas 3.2-4 mm long, somewhat hairy on the lower part, rounded, veins parallel, usually faint, not excurrent, margins smooth or scabrous, margins not white, awnless; palea veins glabrous near the base.

Plants perennial, tufted, not mat forming; culms 1-2.5 dm tall, usually decumbent; leaf blades usually involute, but 0.8-2 mm wide when flat; auricles absent; ligules 0.1-2.8 mm long.

Panicles contracted to diffuse, lowest nodes with 2 branches, spikelets confined to the distal ⅓; pedicels smooth or scabrous; spikelets to 9.5 mm long, 4-5 florets; glumes rounded on the back, veins obscure or distinct, shorter than the florets within them, not papery; calluses glabrous or hairy; lemmas 3.2-4 mm long, hairy on the bases of the veins, apical margins smooth, not white, parallel, awnless; palea veins glabrous, smooth proximally, scabrous distally; anthers 0.8-1.2 mm long.

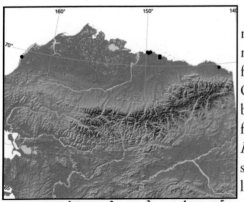

Native low growing grass near the tideline, on disturbed marine sediments or eroded floodplains of the Arctic coast. Often has an unhealthy look because of its decumbent growth form. Unique among the area *Puccinellia* because of its blunt scabrules on the tip of the lemmas.

Anderson's alkali grass
Tribe: Poeae

panicle inflorescence and decumbent growth form

florets

blunt scabrules
lemma tip

spikelets

florets

branch

ligule

lower
glume

upper
glume

Weeping alkali grass
Puccinellia distans (Jacq.) Parl.

Puccinellia hauptiana (Trin. *ex* V. I. Krecz.) Kitag.

Perennial, tufted, not mat forming, culms 0.5-6 dm tall; open-panicle inflorescence; lower branches usually reflexed at maturity; sheaths open, membranous ligule to 3 mm long; spikelets rounded on the back, usually confined to the distal ⅔ of branches, 2-6 florets; glumes not papery, shorter than the multiple florets within them, upper glume 3-nerved, florets disarticulate above the glumes; lemmas soft, nerves parallel, usually faint, not excurrent, margins scabrous, 1.5-2 mm long; palea veins glabrous near the base.

Plants perennial, tufted, not mat forming; culms 0.5-6 dm tall; sheaths open; blades 1-7 mm wide, flat to involute; auricles absent; ligules membranous, 0.8-1.2 mm long.

Panicle pyramidal, loose, 2.5-20 cm long, branches fascicled, rather distant, the lower spreading or reflexed at maturity, spikelets usually confined to distal ⅔; spikelets 2-6 florets; glumes shorter than the multiple perfect florets within them; calluses with a few hairs; lemmas 1.5-2 mm long, rather thin, obtuse or truncate, rather broad toward the apex, with a few short hairs at the base, scabrous near the apex; palea veins glabrous at the base; anthers 0.4-0.8 mm long.

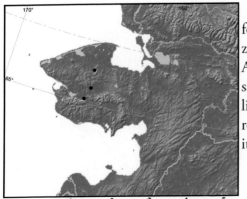

Introduced grass usually found in saturated areas of riparian zones and along salted roadsides. Appears to be a colonizer of new sandy sediment deposits. Used for limited revegetation efforts along roads, attempting to capitalize on its salt tolerance.

Weeping alkali grass
Tribe: Poeae

open panicle inflorescence

lemma margins scabrous near apices

panicle branches

lemmas 1.5-2 mm long

panicle branches horizontal to descending

glumes

spikelets

palea veins glabrous

ligule

anthers 0.4-0.8 mm long

3 veins to upper glume

Sheathed alkali grass
Puccinellia vaginata (Lange) Fernald & Weath.

Perennial, tufted, not mat forming, culms 0.9-2 dm tall; contracted or diffuse panicle inflorescence, branches usually barely exserted from the sheaths at maturity, lower branches ascending to horizontal; membranous ligule, to 3 mm long; spikelets rounded on the back, confined to the distal ⅔ of panicle branches; spikelets usually with 4-5 florets; glumes not papery, shorter than the multiple florets within them, upper glume 3-nerved, lower glume 1.3-2.1 mm long, florets disarticulate above the glumes; lemmas soft, nerves parallel, faint, not excurrent, margins scabrous, 2.8-4 mm long; palea veins glabrous near base.

Plants perennial, tufted, not mat forming; culms 0.9-2 dm tall; sheaths open; blades flat to involute, 1-2 mm wide when flat; auricles absent; ligules membranous, 1-3 mm long.

Panicle contracted to diffuse, 6-12 cm long, barely exserted from the sheath when mature, lower branches ascending to horizontal, spikelets usually confined to distal ⅔; spikelets 4-8 mm long, usually 4-5 florets; lower glume 1.3-2.1 mm long, upper 1.3-2.6 mm long; calluses with a few hairs; lemmas 2.8-4 mm long, thin, often translucent with a few short hairs at the base, scabrous near the apex; palea veins glabrous at the base; anthers 0.7-1.2 mm long.

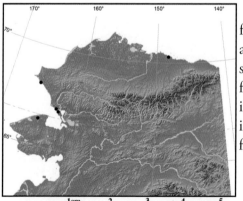

Native low growing grass found on coastal marine sediments and on eroding raised marine sediments inland. Distinguished from *P. tennella* and *P. andersonii* in the field because the inflorescence is barely exserted from the sheath at maturity.

Sheathed alkali grass

Tribe: Poeae

florets

compressed panicle inflorescence

lemmas not often inrolled

anther 0.7 to 1.2 mm long

inflorescence most often remains in the sheath

hairy lemma

spikelets

spikelets

paleas

spikelets

glumes

ligule

Alaska alkali grass, Pacific alkali grass

Puccinellia nutkaensis (J. Presl) Fernald & Weath.

Perennial, tufted, sometimes appearing rhizomatous or stoloniferous when arising from stems buried by sediment at the lower nodes; not mat forming, culms to 9 dm tall; large appressed and compact panicle inflorescence; membranous ligule, to 3 mm long; sheaths open; spikelets rounded on the back, from the base or confined to the upper ½ on panicle branches; spikelets with 3-7 florets; glumes not papery, shorter than the multiple florets within them, upper glume 3-nerved, lower glume 1-1.6 mm long, florets disarticulate above the glumes; lemmas usually 3-4.5 mm long, soft, nerves parallel, not excurrent, faint, margins scabrous; palea veins glabrous near base; pedicels often swollen.

Plants perennial, tufted, at times appearing rhizomatous or stoloniferous, not mat forming; culms 1-9 dm tall; blades flat to involute, 1-6 mm wide when flat; auricles absent; ligules 1-3 mm long.

Panicles 5-30 cm long, appressed, compact, lower branches usually erect to ascending, spikelet-bearing from near the base or spikelets confined to the distal 1/2; pedicels from sparsely to densely scabrous, appearing swollen; spikelets 3.5-12 mm long; lower glume 1-1.6 mm long, upper 2-3 mm long; calluses with a few hairs; lemmas usually 3-4.5 mm long, apical margins uniformly and densely scabrous; anthers 0.5-1.4 mm long.

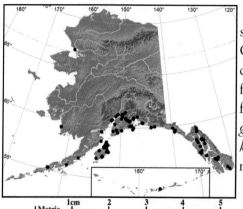

Native grass of sands and sediments just above high tides. Grows on mud flats along Alaska's coast. Is being commercialized for revegetation. Various growth forms resemble *P. hultenii, P. glabra, P. grandis, P. triflora,* and *P. kamtschatica* var. *sublacvis*, which now are included as *P. nutkaensis.*

Alaska alkali grass, Pacific alkali grass

Tribe: Poeae

lower panicle
branches
ascending

panicle
branches

thickened
pedicels

florets

scabrous lemma
margins at apices

lemmas
usually
3-4.5 mm long

ligules

upper glume
3 nerved

glumes

florets

spikelets

Nuttall's alkali grass

Puccinellia nuttalliana (Schult.) Hitchc.

P. borealis Swallen, *P. interior* T.J. Sørensen *ex* Hultén

Perennial, tufted; not mat forming, culms to 10 dm tall; appressed to diffuse and open panicle inflorescence; membranous ligule, to 3 mm long; sheaths open; spikelets rounded on the back, from the base or confined to the upper ⅔ on panicle branches; spikelets with 2-5 florets; glumes not papery, shorter than the multiple florets within them, upper glume 3-nerved, lower glume 0.5-1.5 mm long, florets disarticulate above the glumes; lemmas usually 2.2-3 mm long, soft, nerves parallel, not excurrent, faint, margins scabrous; palea veins glabrous near base; pedicels normal.

Plants perennial, tufted, not mat forming; culms 1-10 dm tall; sheaths open; blades flat to involute, 1-4 mm wide when flat; auricles absent; ligules membranous, 1-3 mm long.

Panicles 5-30 cm long, appressed to diffuse at maturity, lower branches often divergent or reflexed, spikelet-bearing from near the base or spikelets confined to the distal 2/3; pedicels scabrous not appearing swollen; spikelets 3.5-9 mm long; lower glume 0.5-1.5 mm long, upper 1-2.8 mm long; calluses with a few hairs; lemmas usually 2.2-3 mm long, apical margins uniformly and densely scabrous; anthers 0.6-2 mm long.

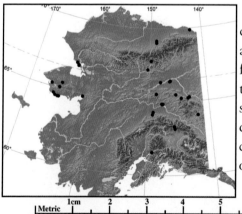

Native grass most common to Interior riparian zones and along roadsides, but also found in coastal areas. Salt tolerant. Colonizer of new saturated stream sediment deposits where it is eventually crowded out by tall sedges and other more competitive grasses.

Nuttall's alkali grass
Tribe: Poeae

Puccinellia nuttalliana

florets

lemma nerves parallel

glumes

ligule

upper glume 3 nerves

open panicle inflorescence branch spikelets

florets

lower glume

upper glume

Foxtail barley

Hordeum jubatum L. subsp. *jubatum*

Perennial, tufted; ligule membranous; spike inflorescence 3-15 cm long, spreading when mature; spikelets 3 per rachis node, arranged on opposite sides of a simple rachis, the center a perfect floret and sessile to the rachis, the lateral pedicelled; awns flexuous, 35-90 mm long.

Plants perennial, tufted; culms 2-8 dm tall; sheaths open; blades to 15 cm long, 6 mm wide, flat; auricles absent; ligules membranous, 0.8 mm long.

Spike inflorescence usually nodding when mature, to 15 cm long, often about as wide, pale; lateral spikelets reduced to 1-3 spreading awns, spikelets short pedicelled; glumes of perfect spikelet 35-85 mm long; lemmas 4-8.5 mm long, awned, awns to 35-90 mm long, ascending to spreading.

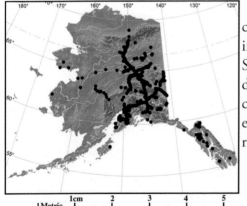

Native grass often considered a weed when growing in cropland and along roadsides. Salt tolerant and prevails in disturbed meadow areas, construction sites, edges of ephemeral reservoirs, and along roadsides.

Foxtail barley
Tribe: Triticeae

spike inflorescence

slender and
flexuous awns
35-90 mm long

lateral
spikelet

lateral
spikelet

3 spikelets at a joint in the rachis

central and
fertile spikelet

ligule

pedicelled, lateral
and sterile spikelets

315

Intermediate barley; Mexican barley

Hordeum jubatum subsp. *intermedium* Bowden

H. caespitosum Scribn., *H. intermedium* Hausskn.

Perennial, tufted; ligule membranous; spike inflorescence 3-15 cm long, somewhat narrow; spikelets 3 per rachis node, arranged on opposite sides of a simple rachis, the center a perfect floret and sessile to the rachis, the lateral pedicelled; awns flexuous, 11-35 mm long.

Plants perennial, tufted; culms 2-8 dm tall; sheaths open; blades to 15 cm long, 6 mm wide, flat; auricles absent; ligules membranous, 0.8 mm long.

Spike inflorescence usually nodding when mature, to 15 cm long, somewhat narrow, pale; lateral spikelets reduced to 1-3 spreading and flexuous awns, spikelets short pedicelled; glumes of perfect spikelet 15-35 mm long; lemmas 4-8.5 mm long, awned, awns 11-35 mm long, ascending to spreading.

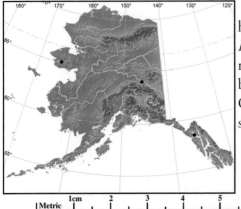

Native riparian grass. A hybrid of *H. jubatum* (p. 314) and *H. brachyantherum* (p. 318), with most characteristics intermediate between the two species. Common when both parent species are nearby.

Intermediate barley; Mexican barley
Tribe: Triticeae

spike inflorescence

ligule

fertile floret

awns 11-35 mm long

sterile florets

three spikelets
at a joint in rachis

Meadow barley
Hordeum brachyantherum Nevski

Perennial, loosely to densely tufted; ligule membranous; spike inflorescence 3-8.5 cm long, narrow, less than 5 cm wide; spikelets 3 per rachis node, arranged on opposite sides of a simple rachis, the center a perfect floret sessile to the rachis, the lateral pedicelled; glumes as awns to 17 mm long; lemma awns to 6.5 mm long, stiff.

Plants perennial, tufted; culms to 9.5 dm tall; sheaths open; blades to 19 cm long, 8 mm wide, flat; auricles absent; ligules membranous, 0.3-0.5 mm long.

Spike 3-8.5 cm long, narrow, rachis disarticulating; spikelets with central one sessile and perfect, lateral pedicelled and sterile; glumes all setaceous or awnlike, about 7-17 mm long; lemmas of middle and perfect spikelet 5.5-10 mm long, scabrous, the awn to 6.5 mm long, stiff and usually straight at maturity.

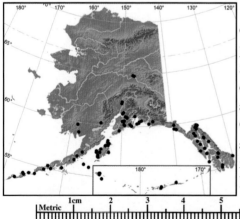

Native riparian grass common to the wetter areas along perennial streams, seeps, springs, meadows, mud flats, and sand dunes of Southeast, Southcentral, and the Aleutian chain of Alaska. Often occurs with beach wildrye and is commercialized and marketed as Lowell Point Meadow Barley.

Meadow barley
Tribe: Triticeae

spike inflorescence

3 spikelets at a joint in the rachis

central and fertile spikelet

short slender awns

pedicelled, lateral and sterile spikelets

ligule

Sixrow barley
Hordeum vulgare L.

Annual; culms 10-15 dm tall; ligule membranous; auricles present; narrow-spike inflorescence, exserted; spikelets 3 per rachis node, all appear sessile, each generally perfect, arranged on opposite sides of a simple continuous rachis; glumes of the fertile spikelets not dilated above the base.

Plants annual; culms 10-15 dm tall; sheaths open; blades 5-18 mm wide, 10-30 cm long, flat, glabrous; auricles 4-4.3 mm long; ligules membranous, 0.8-1.5 mm long.

Spike 5-10 cm long, to 2 cm wide, dense, erect, continuous, not disarticulating; spikelets 3 at a node, all appear sessile, usually all perfect; glumes equal, to 30 mm long, narrow, divergent at base with an awn 7-10 mm long; lemmas to 12 mm long, fusiform or lanceolate, narrowed into a scabrous awn to 180 mm long; paleas about as long as the lemmas.

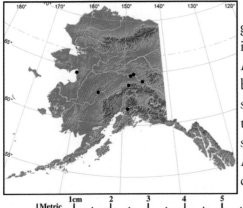

An introduced cultivated grass common to low elevation irrigated basin croplands. *Hordeum distichum* or two-row barley is also cultivated in the same general areas, but differs in that the 2 lateral spikelets are sterile and much reduced. *H. vulgare* is the most common cereal crop in Alaska.

Sixrow barley
Tribe: Triticeae

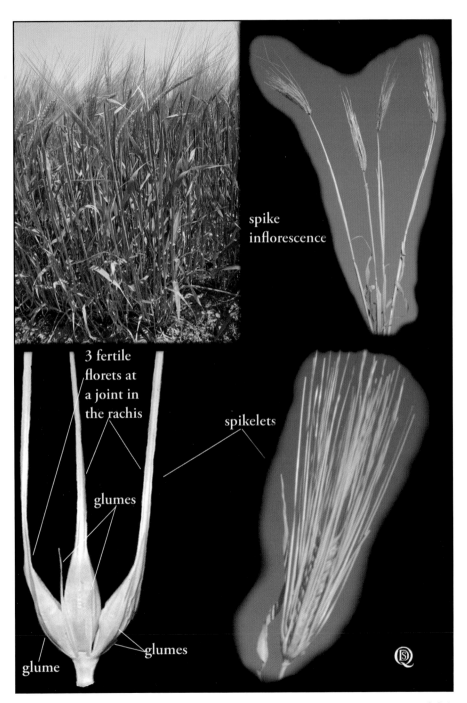

spike
inflorescence

3 fertile
florets at
a joint in
the rachis

spikelets

glumes

glumes

glume

321

Mouse barley; Rabbit barley

Hordeum murinum subsp. *leporinum* (Link) Arcang.
Hordeum leporinum Link

Annual; culms to 11 dm tall; narrow-spike inflorescence, partially enclosed by upper sheath, rachis disarticulating at maturity; auricles present; spikelets 3 per rachis node, arranged on opposite sides of a simple rachis, the center spikelet pedicelled with a perfect floret, lateral spikelets staminate; lemmas of the central florets much shorter than those of the lateral florets.

Plants annual; culms to 11 dm tall, usually erect, sometimes almost prostrate; sheaths open; blades to 28 cm long, flat; auricles to 8 mm long; ligules membranous, 1-4 mm long.

Spike 3-8 cm long, to 16 mm wide, often partly enclosed by the inflated uppermost sheath; rachis internodes mostly 3 mm long, rachis disarticulating at maturity; 3 spikelets at a rachis node, the central pedicellate, pedicels to 2 mm long, floret perfect; lemmas of the central and perfect florets much shorter than those of the lateral florets, to 14 mm long, 2 mm wide, awns to 40 mm long; lateral spikelets staminate, glumes flattened, floret sessile, margins ciliate; lemmas to 15 mm long, awned, awns to 50 mm long.

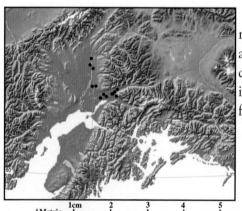

Introduced grass generally restricted to disturbed areas associated with farming, construction, and city infrastructure such as harbor facilities.

Mouse barley; Rabbit barley
Tribe: Triticeae

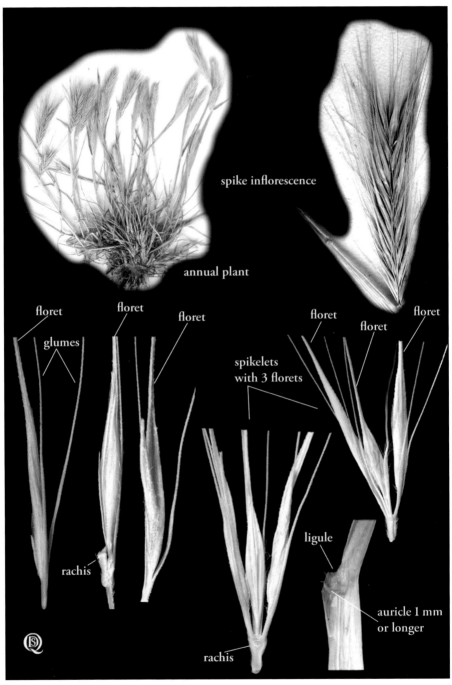

spike inflorescence

annual plant

floret

floret

floret

glumes

floret

floret

floret

spikelets
with 3 florets

rachis

rachis

ligule

auricle 1 mm
or longer

323

Bread wheat

Triticum aestivum L.

Annual; spike inflorescence; ligules membranous; spikelets 1 per rachis node, arranged on opposite sides of the rachis, both spikelet glumes lateral to the rachis; spikes wide and compressed, rachis not disarticulating at maturity; usually 3 or more florets per spikelet; both glumes ovate.

Plants annual; culms to 15 dm tall, erect; sheaths open; blades usually 10-25 cm long, to 15 mm wide, flat; auricles 1.1-1.6 mm long; ligules membranous, 0.8-1.8 mm long.

Inflorescence a dense spike, to 18 cm long, internodes of rachis 3-6 mm long; spikelets broad, 2-5 seed forming florets, to 15 mm long; glumes subequal, broad and asymmetrical, 6-12 mm long, usually strongly keeled toward one side, the keel extending into a mucro, the other side usually obtusely angled at the apex; lemmas to 15 mm long, broad, keeled, asymmetrical, more or less 3-toothed at apex, the middle extending into an antrorsely scabrous awn to 12 cm long (awnless in some types); paleas about as long as the lemmas, not splitting at maturity.

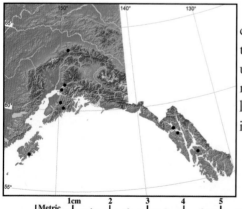

Introduced annual grass cultivated at lower elevations for the grain, flour, and forage. Also used as a cover crop for reclamation of disturbed landscapes. Production is limited in Alaska.

324

Bread wheat
Tribe: Triticeae

spike inflorescence

fertile florets

broad ovate
glumes

rachis

Common rye

Secale cereale L.

Annual; spike a narrow inflorescence, usually nodding when mature; ligules membranous; spikelets 1 per rachis node, arranged on opposite sides of the rachis, both spikelet glumes lateral and appressed to the rachis; rachis not or tardily disarticulating at maturity; usually 2-3 florets per spikelet; both glumes linear to subulate, strongly keeled, 8-20 mm long, awned, awns 1-3 mm long; lemma awns to 50 mm long.

Plants annual; culms usually 5-12 dm tall, erect; sheaths open; blades to 12 mm wide, flat; auricles 0.5-1 mm long; ligules membranous, 0.5-1.1 mm long.

Spikes to 19 cm long, dense; spikelets usually 2-flowered, solitary, placed flatwise against the rachis, the rachilla disarticulating above the glumes and produced beyond the upper floret as a minute stipe; glumes 8-20 mm long, narrow, rigid, acuminate or subulate-pointed; lemmas 14-18 mm long, broader, sharply keeled, 5-nerved, ciliate on the keel and exposed margins, tapering into long awn 7-50 mm long.

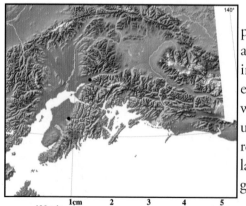

Introduced grass used to produce rye grain for flour, cereal, and whiskey. Cultivated as an irrigated and dryland crop and has escaped to grow along roadsides where water accumulates. Also used as a cover crop for reclamation of disturbed landscapes. The least produced grain crop in Alaska.

Common rye
Tribe: Triticeae

spike inflorescence

2 spikelets
at a joint
in the rachis

spikelet

ligule

glumes

Crested wheatgrass

Agropyron cristatum (L.) Gaertn.

Perennial, tufted, sometimes rhizomatous; spike inflorescence, 5-25 mm wide, somewhat rectangular in shape; spikelets 1 per rachis node, arranged on opposite sides of the rachis, spikelets imbricate, often pectinate, diverging from the rachis at an angle of more than 30-95 degrees; both glumes shorter than the multiple florets within them; lemmas usually awned, awns 1-6 mm long.

Plants perennial, tufted; culms 2.5-11 dm tall, erect to sometimes geniculate; sheaths open; blades to 6 mm wide, flat or involute; auricles 0.2 mm long; ligules membranous, to 1.5 mm long.

Spikes to 15 cm long, 5-25 mm wide, lanceolate, rectangular in shape, sometimes tapering distally, pectinate; spikelets 7-16 mm long, diverging from the rachis at an angle of more than 30-95 degrees, 3-10 florets; glumes 3-5 mm long, ovate-lanceolate, widely spread at an angle of more than 120 degrees from one another when mature, awns 1.5-3 mm long; lemmas 5-9 mm long, awns 1-6 mm long.

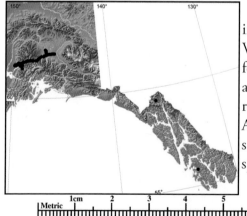

Introduced grass used in range improvement projects. Valued for providing early spring forage for large grazing animals and stabilizing disturbed lands like roadsides and burned areas. Use in Alaska has been limited, and superseded in favor of native species.

Crested wheatgrass
Tribe: Triticeae

spike inflorescence

spikelets imbricate

florets

palea

florets

ligule

lemmas

spikelets

glumes

Fuzzyspike wildrye

Leymus innovatus subsp. *velutinus* (Bowden) Tzvelev
Elymus innovatus Beal

Perennial, strongly rhizomatous, sometimes loosely tufted, not glaucous; ligules membranous; culms to 10.5 dm tall; spike inflorescence; spikelets more than 1 per rachis node, arranged on opposite sides of a simple rachis, sometimes 1 or more pedicelled; two glumes per spikelet, keeled distally, shorter than the multiple perfect florets within them, subulate, broadest near the base, keels offset to the side of the keels on the lemmas; rachis continuous at maturity; lemmas strongly pubescent, awned.

Plants perennial, strongly rhizomatous; culms 6-10.5 dm tall, 2-3 mm thick; sheaths open; blades 2-6 mm wide, involute, sometimes flat; auricles to 1.4 mm long; ligules membranous, 0.2-1.2 mm long.

Spikes 3-8 cm long, 15-20 mm wide, rachis continuous at and after maturity; lower spikelets sometimes distant; spikelets 12-23 mm long, 2-7 florets, crowded above becoming distant below; glumes unequal, very narrow, to 12 mm long, 1 mm wide, awn tipped, pubescent; lemmas to 12 mm long, villous to appressed pubescent, hairs 1.5-2.5 mm long, awn tipped or the awn to 4 mm long.

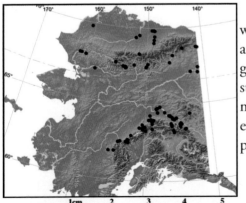

Native grass found in open woods, tall willow communities, and rocky disturbed sites like gravel bars, aggraded gravels of streams draining glaciers, and man-made disturbances. Being evaluated for commercial seed production.

330

Fuzzyspike wildrye
Tribe: Triticeae

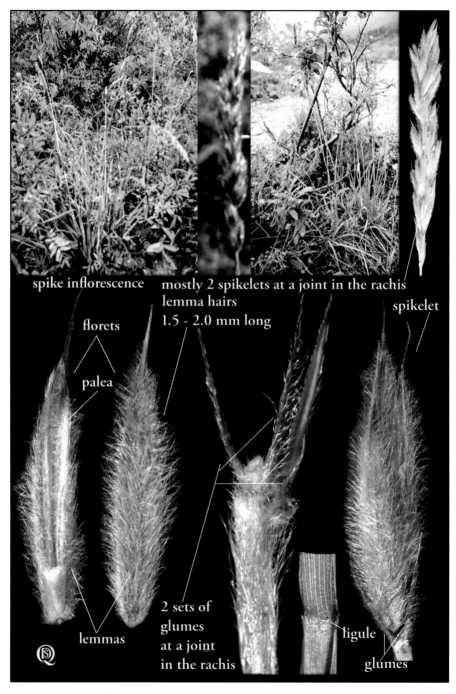

spike inflorescence

mostly 2 spikelets at a joint in the rachis

lemma hairs
1.5 - 2.0 mm long

spikelet

florets

palea

lemmas

2 sets of
glumes
at a joint
in the rachis

ligule

glumes

Beach wildrye, American dunegrass

Leymus mollis (Trin.) Pilg. subsp. *mollis*

Elymus arenarius L., *E. arenarius* subsp. *mollis* (Trin.) Hultén

Perennial, strongly rhizomatous, rhizomes thick; culms to 17 dm tall, often glaucous; ligules membranous; spike inflorescence, spikes 12-34 cm long with 12-33 nodes, rachis continuous at maturity; spikelets more than 1 per rachis node, arranged on opposite sides of a simple rachis; glumes two per spikelet, rounded on the back or somewhat flat, not strongly keeled, about as long or a bit longer than the multiple perfect florets within them, keels offset to the side of the faint keels on the lemmas; lemmas awnless.

Plants perennial, strongly rhizomatous, rhizomes 4-6 mm thick; culms 7-17 dm tall, to 6 mm thick; sheaths open; basal blades 22-94 cm long, 5-15 mm wide; auricles to 0.7 mm long; ligules membranous, 1.5-2.5 mm long.

Spikes 12-34 cm long, 10-20 mm wide, with 12-33 nodes, rachis continuous at and after maturity; lower spikelets sometimes distant; spikelets 15-34 mm long, 3-6 florets; glumes unequal, flat or rounded on the back, 9-34 mm long, 1.5-4 mm wide, apices acuminate; lemmas to 20 mm long, densely villous, hairs 0.5-1 mm long, awnless.

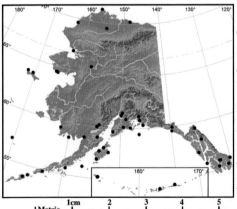

Native grass found along coastal beaches close to the high tideline. The primary dune colonizer in Alaska and used for beach stabilization and reclamation of disturbed sites. Most reclamation is accomplished using transplants. Provides some value as winter forage for herbivores.

Beach wildrye, American dunegrass
Tribe: Triticeae

spike inflorescence 2 spikelets at a joint in the rachis rhizome

ligule

florets

palea

lemmas rachilla

the 2 sets of glumes
at a rachis node

2 spikelets
at a rachis node

Beach wildrye, American dunegrass

Leymus mollis subsp. *villosissimus* (Scribn.) Á. Löve

Perennial, strongly rhizomatous, rhizomes thin; culms to 7 dm tall, often glaucous; ligules membranous; spike inflorescence, spikes usually 5-13 cm long with 3-14 nodes, rachis continuous at maturity; spikelets more than 1 per rachis node, arranged on opposite sides of a simple rachis; glumes two per spikelet, rounded on the back or somewhat flat, not strongly keeled, about as long or a bit longer than the multiple perfect florets within them, keels offset to the side of the faint keels on the lemmas; lemmas awnless.

Plants perennial, strongly rhizomatous, rhizomes about 2 mm thick; culms to 7 dm tall, to 6 mm thick; sheaths open; basal blades 10-31 cm long, 3-8 mm wide; auricles to 0.7 mm long; ligules membranous, 1.5-2.5 mm long.

Spikes 5-13 cm long, 10-20 mm wide, with 3-14 nodes, rachis continuous at and after maturity; lower spikelets sometimes distant; spikelets 15-34 mm long, 3-6 florets; glumes unequal, flat or rounded on the back, 9-14 mm long, 1.5-2.5 mm wide, apices acuminate, often longer than the lemmas; lemmas to 14 mm long, densely villous, hairs 0.5-1 mm long, awnless.

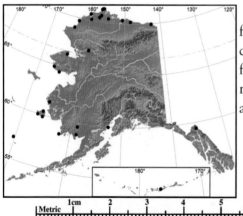

Native grass generally found along Arctic coastal beaches close to the high tideline. Used for beach stabilization and reclamation of coastal disturbed areas.

Beach wildrye, American dunegrass
Tribe: Triticeae

spike inflorescence   2 spikelets at a joint in the rachis   3-14 joints in
ligule   2 sets of glumes   the rachis

lemmas

palea

florets

glumes
as long
or longer
than florets

335

Common quackgrass

Elymus repens (L.) Gould

Elytrigia repens (L.) Desv. *ex* Nevski; *Agropyron repens* (L.) P. Beauv.

Perennial, strongly rhizomatous; ligules membranous; spike inflorescence; spikelets 1 per rachis node, arranged on opposite sides of a simple rachis, glumes 2 for each spikelet, shorter than the multiple perfect florets within them, their keels in line with the keels of the lowest lemmas, broadest at or above the middle; leaf blades finely veined adaxially, major and minor veins definitely differing in height; anthers 4-7 mm long.

Plants perennial, strongly rhizomatous; culms to 10 dm tall; sheaths open; leaf blades 6-10 mm wide, flat, finely veined, veins varying in height adaxially; auricles rudimentary to 0.8 mm long; ligules membranous, 0.4-0.7 mm long.

Spikes 5-15 cm long; spikelets 10-27 mm long, 4- to 7-flowered; glumes subequal, equaling about one-half the spikelet, 3- to 7-nerved and usually awn-tipped; lemmas 8-12 mm long, glabrous, sometimes scabrous, awnless, or the awn 0.2-4 mm long, straight; anthers 4-7 mm long.

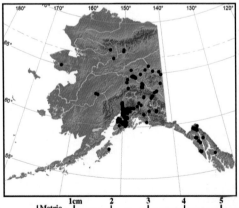

Introduced grass common to gardens, irrigated pastures, agricultural areas, along ditches, and in moist to wet roadsides. Often considered a noxious weed because it persists from large, multiple rhizomes causing damage to crops and displacing native species.

Common quackgrass
Tribe: Triticeae

ligules

spike inflorescence

strongly rhizomatous

leaf blade finely veined adaxially

leaf veins of different heights

florets

palea

palea

lemma

spikelets of 2 collections

palea

glumes

glumes

lemmas

One-sided wheatgrass, Bearded slender wheatgrass

Elymus trachycaulus subsp. *subsecundus* (Link) Á. Löve, D. Löve
Agropyron subsecundum (Link) Hitchc.

Perennial, tufted; ligules membranous; spike inflorescence; spikelets 1 per rachis node, arranged on opposite sides of a simple rachis, usually twisted so it appears somewhat 1-sided; glumes 2 for each spikelet, shorter than the multiple perfect florets within them, their keels in line with the keels of the lowest lemmas, broadest at or above the middle; lemma awns longer than the body of the lemma; anthers usually 1.2-2.5 mm long.

Plants perennial, usually tufted, sometimes weakly rhizomatous; culms 4-11 dm tall; sheaths open; leaf blades 2-5 mm wide, flat to involute; auricles absent to 1 mm long, ligules membranous, 0.2-0.8 mm long.

Spikes 7-25 cm long, slender, usually twisted so appear somewhat one sided; spikelets usually 9-17 mm long, 3-7 florets, distant or partially or closely imbricate, the bases usually visible; glumes 11-17 mm long, long acuminate or awned, awns to 11 mm long; lemmas awned, awns 17-40 mm long, straight.

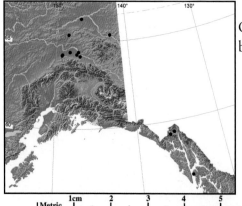

Common grass of the Great Plains. Appears to have been introduced to Alaska.

338

One-sided wheatgrass, Bearded slender wheatgrass
Tribe: Triticeae

lemma

palea

florets

some
hairs

spike inflorescence

ligule

auricle

one spikelet at joint
in the rachis

florets

awn longer
than lemma

glabrous

lemma

glumes

spikelet

Northern wheatgrass

Elymus macrourus (Turcz. ex Steud.) Tzvelev
Agropyron macrourum (Turcz.) Drobow

Perennial, tufted; ligules membranous; spike inflorescence; spikelets 1 per rachis node, arranged on opposite sides of a simple rachis, appearing 2 sided; glumes 2 for each spikelet, shorter than the multiple perfect florets within them, ⅓-⅔ as long as their adjacent lemmas, their keels in line with the keels of the lowest lemmas, lanceolate, broadest at or above the middle, 0.8-1.8 mm wide, awnless or awns to 1 mm long, margins subequal; rachillas hairy; lemmas 8-12 mm long, hairy throughout or glabrous distally, hairs all alike, awnless or awns to 7 mm long; anthers usually 1-2 mm long.

Plants perennial, tufted, sometimes weakly rhizomatous; culms 3.5-10 dm tall, ascending to erect; sheaths open; blades 3-10 mm wide, flat; auricles absent; ligules 0.5-1 mm long.

Spikes 5-20 cm long, 0.4-0.8 cm wide, erect, one spikelet per node; spikelets 12-20 mm long, appressed, 4-to 7-flowered; rachillas hairy, hairs 0.3-0.5 mm long; glumes ⅓-⅔ as long as their adjacent lemmas, 0.8-1.8 mm wide, margins subequal, about 0.3 mm wide, awnless or awns to 1 mm long; lemmas 8-12 mm long, hairy throughout or glabrous distally, hairs alike, 0.2-0.3 mm long, awnless or awned, awns to 7 mm long, straight; anthers 1-2 mm long.

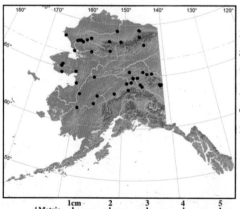

Native grass growing on riverbanks and bars, lakeshores, and rocky hillsides throughout the Interior and western Alaska. Mostly tufted, but when growing on shifting riverbanks or bars, it may appear rhizomatous.

Northern wheatgrass
Tribe: Triticeae

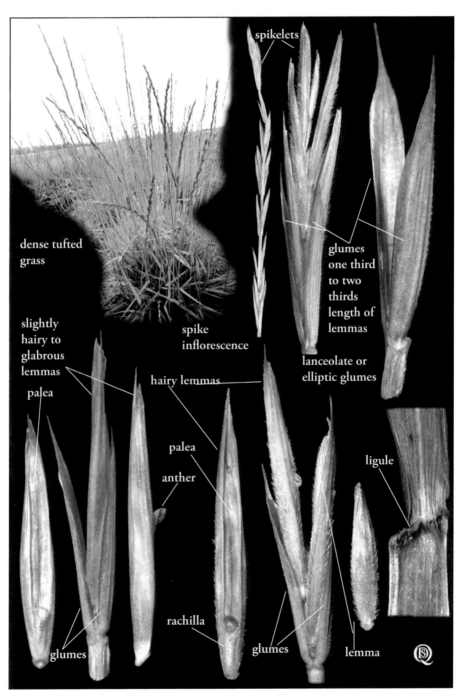

spikelets

dense tufted grass

glumes one third to two thirds length of lemmas

slightly hairy to glabrous lemmas

spike inflorescence

lanceolate or elliptic glumes

palea

hairy lemmas

palea

anther

ligule

glumes

rachilla

glumes

lemma

High-arctic wheatgrass

Elymus alaskanus subsp. *hyperarcticus* (Polunin) Á. Löve, D. Löve

Agropyron boreale subsp. *hyperarcticum* (Polunin) Melderis

Perennial, tufted; ligules membranous; spike inflorescence; spikelets 1 per rachis node, arranged on opposite sides of a simple rachis, appearing 2 sided; glumes 2 for each spikelet, shorter than the multiple perfect florets within them, 1/3-2/3 as long as their adjacent lemmas, their keels in line with the keels of the lowest lemmas, oblanceolate to obovate, broadest at or above the middle, 1.5-2 mm wide, awnless or awns to 1 mm long, margins unequal, densely hairy; rachillas hispidulous; lemmas 7-11 mm long, densely hairy, hairs 0.2-0.5 mm long, awns 1-5 mm long, straight.

Plants perennial, tufted, sometimes weakly rhizomatous; culms usually 2-3.5 dm tall, ascending to erect; sheaths open; blades 2.5-5 mm wide, flat; auricles absent; ligules 0.5-1 mm long.

Spikes 4.5-7 cm long, 0.5-0.8 cm wide, erect or nodding distally, one spikelet per node; spikelets usually 9-15 mm long, appressed, 3-to 6-flowered; rachillas hispidulous; glumes ⅓-⅔ the length of their adjacent lemmas, oblanceolate to obovate, flat, usually purplish, margins unequal, widest margin 0.4-1 mm wide, both margins widest above the middle, awnless or awns to 1 mm long; lemmas 7-11 mm long, densely hairy throughout, hairs 0.2-0.5 mm long, awns to 5 mm long, straight; anthers 1-2 mm long.

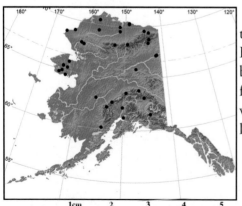

Native grass common throughout dry regions of Alaska. Found on dry riverbanks, river bars, disturbed areas caused by frost heaving, dry rocky areas, as well as man-made disturbances like airstrips and roadsides.

342

High-arctic wheatgrass
Tribe: Triticeae

spike inflorescence

ligule

anther

spikelet

glumes and lemmas densely hairy

lemma

palea

rachilla

lemma

glumes

glumes 1/3-2/3 as long as adjacent lemmas

343

Alaskan wheatgrass

Elymus alaskanus (Scrib. & Merr.) Á. Löve subsp. *alaskanus*

Agropyron boreale (Turcz.) Drobow

Perennial, tufted; ligules membranous; spike inflorescence; spikelets 1 per rachis node, arranged on opposite sides of a simple rachis, appearing 2 sided; glumes 2 for each spikelet, shorter than the multiple perfect florets within them, 1/3-2/3 as long as their adjacent lemmas, their keels in line with the keels of the lowest lemmas, oblanceolate to obovate, broadest at or above the middle, 1.5-2 mm wide, awnless or awns to 1 mm long, margins unequal, glabrous to sparsely hairy; rachillas hispidulous; lemmas 7-11 mm long, glabrous or hairy distally, hairs 0.2 mm long, awns to 7 mm long, straight.

Plants perennial, tufted, sometimes weakly rhizomatous; culms 2-9 dm tall, sometimes decumbent at the base, upper part ascending to erect; sheaths open; blades 3-7 mm wide, flat; auricles absent or to 0.5 mm long; ligules 0.2-0.6 mm long.

Spikes 3.5-14 cm long, 0.5-0.8 cm wide, erect distally, one spikelet per node; spikelets usually 9-15 mm long, appressed, 3-to 6-flowered; rachillas hispidulous; glumes 1/3-2/3 the length of their adjacent lemmas, usually purplish, margins unequal, widest margin 0.4-1 mm wide, both margins widest above the middle, awnless or awns to 1 mm long; lemmas 7-11 mm long, glabrous to hairy distally, hairs 0.2 mm long, awns to 7 mm long, straight; anthers 1-2 mm long.

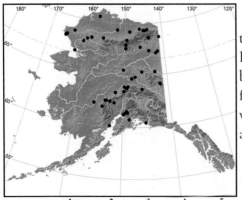

Native grass common throughout dry regions of Alaska. Found on dry riverbanks, river bars, disturbed areas caused by frost heaving, dry rocky areas, as well as man-made disturbances like airstrips and roadsides.

Alaskan wheatgrass
Tribe: Triticeae

floret hairy distally

glabrous near callus

palea

lemma

spike inflorescence

spikelet

hairy culm nodes

single spikelet at node in the rachis

ligule

rachilla

glumes

345

Arctic wheatgrass

Elymus violaceus (Hornem.) Feilberg

Agropyron violaceum (Hornem.) Lange subsp. *violaceum*

Perennial, tufted; ligules membranous; spike inflorescence; spikelets 1 per rachis node, arranged on opposite sides of a simple rachis, appearing 2 sided; glumes 2 for each spikelet, shorter than the multiple perfect florets within them, ¾ as long as their adjacent lemmas, their keels in line with the keels of the lowest lemmas, broadest at or above the middle, margins unequal, 3-5 nerved, awnless or awns to 2 mm long; lemmas usually glabrous, awnless or awns 0.5-3 mm long, straight.

Plants perennial, tufted; culms 1.8-7.5 dm tall, often decumbent or geniculate; sheaths open; blades 3-4 mm wide, flat; auricles to 0.5 mm long; ligules 0.5-1 mm long.

Spikes 5-12 cm long, 0.4-0.7 cm wide excluding the awns, erect, one spikelet per node; spikelets usually 11-19 mm long, appressed, 3-to 5-flowered; rachillas hairy; glumes 3/4 the length of the spikelets, 8-12 mm long, 3-5 veined, narrowly ovate to obovate, often purplish, flat, margins unequal, widest margin 0.3-1 mm wide, both margins widest above the middle, awnless or awns to 2 mm long; lemmas glabrous to somewhat hairy, awned, awns 0.5-3 mm long, straight; anthers 0.7-1.3 mm long.

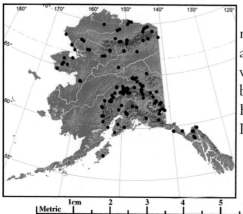

Native grass of higher mountain elevations and drier areas of tundra. Has been placed with *E. trachycaulus* as a subspecies, but is now listed as its own species. Found primarily in Southcentral, Interior, and Arctic areas of Alaska.

ligule

one spikelet at a joint in the rachis

spikelet

spike inflorescence

lemma

florets

palea

hairy rachilla

more hairs at the base of the floret than at the apical end

glumes

Slender wheatgrass

Elymus trachycaulus (Link) Gould subsp. *trachycaulus*

Agropyron pauciflorum Schur

Perennial, tufted, sometimes weakly rhizomatous; ligules membranous; spike inflorescence; spikelets 1 per rachis node, arranged on opposite sides of a simple rachis, appearing 2 sided; glumes 2 for each spikelet, shorter than the multiple perfect florets within them, ¾ as long as their adjacent lemmas, their keels in line with the keels of the lowest lemmas, broadest at or above the middle, margins subequal, 3-7 nerved, veins scabrous, generally awned, awns to 2 mm long; rachillas glabrous or hairy; lemmas glabrous or pubescent, awns to 5 mm long, straight.

Plants perennial, tufted, sometimes weakly rhizomatous; culms 3-15 dm tall, ascending to erect; sheaths open; blades 2-5 mm wide, flat to involute; auricles absent or to 1 mm long; ligules 0.2-0.8 mm long.

Spikes 8-30 cm long, 0.5-0.8 cm wide excluding the awns, erect, one spikelet per node; spikelets usually 9-17 mm long, appressed, 3-9 florets; rachillas glabrous or hairy; glumes ¾ the length of the spikelets, 5-17 mm long, 3-7 nerved, lanceolate to narrowly ovate, green at lower elevations, purplish at higher elevations, flat, margins subequal, awns to 2 mm long; lemmas glabrous, awnless or awns to 5 mm long, straight; anthers 1.2-2.5 mm long.

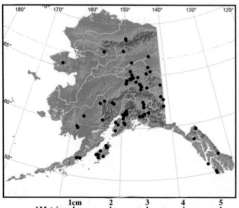

Native grass common to a wide variety of elevations and habitats in Alaska. Recognized by its longer glumes and their subequal margins. The cultivar 'Wainwright' is Alaska's most produced agricultural native grass crop. Used extensively for road and airport seedings.

Slender wheatgrass
Tribe: Triticeae

spikelets

spikelets distant from each other

glumes green 3-7 nerves

lemma awns to 5 mm long

glumes

lower glume

upper glume

ligule

florets

lemma

palea

spike inflorescence

glumes

rachilla

Siberian wildrye
Elymus sibiricus L.

Perennial, tufted, sometimes weakly rhizomatous, usually glaucous; ligules membranous; spike inflorescence, nodding to pendent at maturity; spikelets usually 2 or more per rachis node, arranged on opposite sides of a simple rachis; two glumes per spikelet, body shorter than the multiple perfect florets within them, linear-lanceolate, with flat bases; lemmas densely scabridulous to scabrous, awned, awns curving out at maturity; anthers 0.9-1.7 mm long.

Plants perennial, tufted, sometimes rhizomatous; culms 4-15 dm tall, erect or slightly geniculate at the base; sheaths open; blades 4-14 mm wide, lax, flat; auricles to 1 mm long, often absent; ligules usually to 1 mm long.

Spikes 7-30 cm long, 2-5 cm wide, usually nodding to pendent, usually two spikelets per node; spikelets 10-18 mm long, appressed to divergent, usually 4-5 florets; glumes 3-8 mm long excluding the awns, the base flat, not hard, awns 1-6 mm long, straight; lemmas 8-13 mm long, densely scabridulous to scabrous, awns 10-25 mm long, somewhat outcurving from the base; anthers 0.9-1.7 mm long.

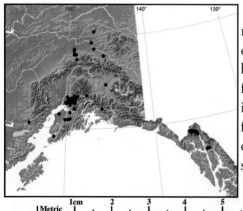

Introduced or perhaps native grass found on moist disturbed sites from coastal beaches to forest margins. Often found near agricultural areas where it has been evaluated as a potential forage crop. Its status as a native or introduced grass in Alaska is not settled.

350

Siberian wildrye
Tribe: Triticeae

florets
lemma
palea
lemma
rachilla
spike inflorescence
spikelets
spikelet
glumes
glumes
2 spikelets at a rachis node
ligule

Northwestern wildrye
Elymus hirsutus J. Presl

Perennial, tufted, sometimes weakly rhizomatous; ligules membranous; auricles absent to 1.5 mm long; spike inflorescence, nodding to pendent at maturity; auricles absent to 1.5 mm long; spikelets usually 2 or more per rachis node, arranged on opposite sides of a simple rachis; two glumes per spikelet, body shorter than the multiple perfect florets within them, bodies usually 7-10 mm long, · linear-lanceolate, with flat bases; lemmas densely scabridulous to scabrous, awned, awns curving out at maturity; anthers 2-3.5 mm long.

Plants perennial, tufted, sometimes rhizomatous; culms 4-14 dm tall, erect or slightly geniculate at the base; sheaths open; blades 4-12 mm wide, lax, flat; auricles to 1.5 mm long, often absent; ligules to 1 mm long.

Spikes 6-20 cm long, 0.5-2 cm wide, nodding to pendent, usually two spikelets per node; spikelets 12-20 mm long, appressed to divergent, usually 2-4 florets; glume bodies 7-10 mm long, the base flat, not hard, awns usually 1-10 mm long, straight; lemmas 7-14 mm long, smooth or scabridulous, awns usually 8-30 mm long, somewhat outcurving; anthers 2-3.5 mm long.

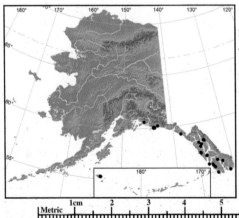

Native grass of coastal forest margins or within damp woods along coastal mountains. Easily recognized by its tall stature and nodding to pendent spikes.

Northwestern wildrye
Tribe: Triticeae

spike inflorescence

ligule

flat base of glumes

spikelet glumes

florets

spikelets

florets

lemma

palea

2 spikelets at a joint in the rachis

anther

glumes

stigma

1 spikelet

glumes

Blue wildrye

Elymus glaucus subsp. *virescens* (Piper) Gould

Perennial, tufted, sometimes weakly rhizomatous, usually glaucous; ligules membranous; spike inflorescence, erect to slightly nodding at maturity; spikelets usually 2 per rachis node, arranged on opposite sides of a simple rachis; two glumes per spikelet, body just shorter or equal to the multiple perfect florets within them, bodies 9-14 mm long, awns 0-2 mm long, linear-lanceolate, with flat bases; lemmas densely scabridulous to scabrous, awns usually 1-5 mm long, usually straight; anthers 1.5-3.5 mm long.

Plants perennial, densely to loosely tufted, sometimes rhizomatous; culms usually 3-14 dm tall, erect or slightly decumbent; sheaths open; blades 2-10 mm wide, lax, flat, sometimes involute; auricles to 2.5 mm long, usually present; ligules usually to 1 mm long.

Spikes 5-21 cm long, 0.5-2 cm wide, erect to slightly nodding, usually two spikelets per node; spikelets 8-25 mm long, appressed to slightly divergent, usually 2-to 4-flowered; glumes 3/4 to as long as the adjacent lemmas, the base flat, not hard, bodies 9-14 mm long, awnless or awned, awns 0-2 mm long, straight; lemmas usually 9-14 mm long, smooth or scabridulous to pubescent, awns usually 1-5 mm long, straight; anthers 1.5-3.5 mm long.

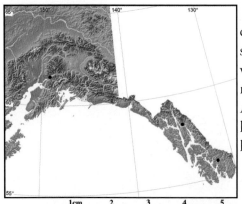

Native grass found on drier soils at the base of cliffs, slopes, lakeshores, riverbanks, and within forests and along their margins. Often confused with *Elymus trachycaulus,* but has wider, lax, and flatter leaves, and usually has 2 spikelets at some nodes.

Blue wildrye
Tribe: Triticeae

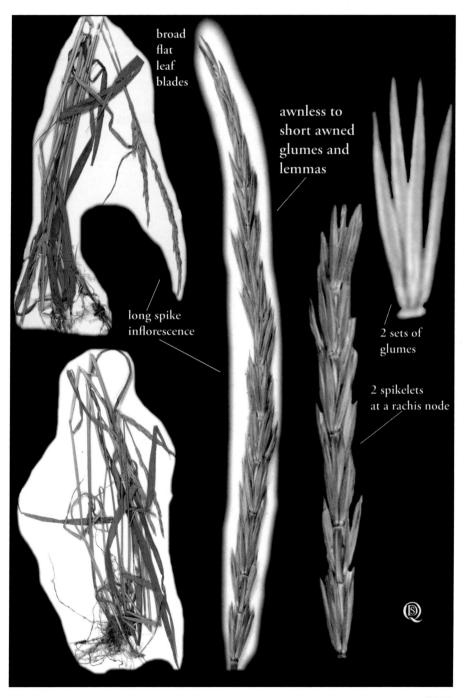

broad
flat
leaf
blades

awnless to
short awned
glumes and
lemmas

2 sets of
glumes

2 spikelets
at a rachis node

long spike
inflorescence

Blue wildrye

Elymus glaucus Buckley subsp. *glaucus*

Perennial, tufted, sometimes weakly rhizomatous, usually glaucous; ligules membranous; auricles usually present, to 2.5 mm long; spike inflorescence, erect to slightly nodding at maturity; spikelets usually 2 per rachis node, arranged on opposite sides of a simple rachis; two glumes per spikelet, body just shorter or equal to the multiple perfect florets within them, bodies 9-14 mm long, awns 1-5 mm long, linear-lanceolate, glumes with flat bases; lemmas densely scabridulous to scabrous, awns 10-25 mm long, usually straight; anthers 1.5-3.5 mm long.

Plants perennial, densely to loosely tufted, sometimes rhizomatous; culms 3-14 dm tall, erect or slightly decumbent; sheaths open; blades 4-17 mm wide, lax, flat, sometimes involute; auricles to 2.5 mm long, usually present; ligules to 1 mm long.

Spikes 5-21 cm long, 0.5-2 cm wide, erect to slightly nodding, usually two spikelets per node; spikelets 8-25 mm long, appressed to slightly divergent, usually 2-4 florets; glumes ¾ to as long as the adjacent lemmas, the base flat, not hard, bodies 9-14 mm long, awned, awns to 5 mm long, straight; lemmas 9-14 mm long, smooth or scabridulous to pubescent, awns 10-25 mm long, usually straight; anthers 1.5-3.5 mm long.

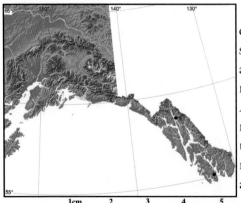

Native grass found on drier soils at the base of cliffs, slopes, lake shores, river banks, and within forests and along their margins. Often confused with *Elymus trachycaulus,* but has wider, more lax and flatter leaves, usually has 2 spikelets at some nodes, and the glumes are usually awned.

356

Blue wildrye
Tribe: Triticeae

spike inflorescence

awned florets

florets

spikelet

ligules

glumes

multiple spikelets at a joint
in the rachis

glumes

Glossary

Abaxial: The opposite side to, or facing away from, the axis of an organ.

Above: In the upper part.

Acuminate: Gradually tapering to a point, the sides concave before reaching the point.

Acute: Tapering to a point with the sides more or less straight.

Adaxial: The side facing the axis of an organ.

Annual: Completes its life cycle (germination, flowering, and seed-set) in one growing season.

Anther: Pollen-bearing organ at the tip of a stamen.

Anthesis: Period when the flower is expanded for pollination.

Anthocyanic: Containing water soluble blue, purple, and red pigments.

Antrorse: Pointed forward or upward.

Apex: Tip.

Apical: At or referring to the tip.

Apiculate: Abruptly ending in a short point.

Appressed: Flattened against.

Approximate: Near or close to.

Aristate: Awned from the tip.

Ascending: Growing upward at an angle.

Attenuate: Narrowing to a long slender point.

Auricles: Projecting appendages at the base of the leaf blade.

Awn: Bristle growing from the tip or back of a glume or lemma, and at times palea, usually an extension of a nerve.

Axillary: Growing from between a stem and the base of a leaf.

Axis: Rachis; the main stem of the inflorescence; the culm.

Bearded: Bearing long, often stiff, hairs.

358

Below: In the lower part.

Bi-: Latin prefix meaning two.

Bidentate: With two teeth at the tip.

Bifid: Two-cleft or two-lobed at the tip, usually fairly deeply.

Blade: Free terminal part of a leaf above the sheath.

Boat shaped: Keeled like a boat.

Boat tipped: Having a tip shaped like the prow of a boat.

Bract: Modified leaf; in grasses, the glumes, lemmas, paleas, or part of an involucre.

Bristle: Very stiff hair; in grasses, sometimes used in place of awn, but more commonly used to refer to a modified inflorescence branch.

Bud: An undeveloped leaf or flower.

Bulb: Swollen lower internode or internodes of the culm in some grasses used for carbohydrate storage; actually a corm rather than a true bulb in grasses.

Bulbil: Small leaf-life or bulb-like organ developing in place of the flower; used as a means of vegetative reproduction (see pseudovivipary).

Bulblet: Small bulb-like or leaf-like organ developing in place of the flower; used as a means of vegetative reproduction.

Bunchgrass: Caespitose or tufted grass plant forming a clump of culms and basal leaves and which, when reproducing vegetatively, sends up shoots from its base.

Bur: Hard, usually spiny, structure surrounding the spikelets or florets, composed of modified inflorescence branches or spikelet parts.

Caespitose, cespitose: Growing in dense bunches or tufts.

Callus: Hardened base of the lemma; a portion of the rachilla left attached to the lemma after the lemma has fallen from the spikelet.

Canescent: With dense, short, gray or white hairs.

Capillary: Very slender and hairlike; usually said of inflorescence branches.

Cartilaginous: Hard and tough but flexible; resembling cartilage.

Caryopsis: Fruit of a grass; a seed surrounded by, and adhering to, the pericarp or ovary wall. In some grasses the seed is free of the pericarp and the fruit is actually an achene.

Chevron: A broad upright or inverted V.

Ciliate: With a fringe of hairs on the margin.

Ciliolate: With a fringe of very short hairs on the margin.

Cleistogamous: Referring to flowers that are self-fertilized and set seed without opening.

Cleistogene: Flower that is self-fertilized and sets seed without opening, especially one that develops in the sheath and is separate from the inflorescence.

Closed: Dense; not open; of a sheath, the margins fused for more than half their lengths; tightly appressed to the axis.

Collar: Region of the abaxial side of a leaf at the junction of the blade and the sheath, frequently having a different appearance than the rest of the leaf.

Compressed: Flattened.

Compressed-keeled: Laterally flattened, the fold forming a sharp ridge.

Concave: With the surface curved inward or hollowed out.

Constricted: Pinched; of a collar, narrower in the middle than at the ends.

Continuous: Not interrupted; of a rachis, not disarticulating at maturity; of a collar, of the same texture throughout.

Contracted: Narrowed; of an inflorescence, dense with short or appressed branches.

Convex: With the surface curved outward; rounded.

Convolute: Rolled lengthwise, especially with one edge overlapping the other; frequently used as a synonym for involute.

Cool season: Plant which grows and matures early in the growing season.

Cordate: Heart shaped with the notch at the base.

Coriaceous: Leathery in texture.

Corm: Swollen lower culm internode or internodes used in carbohydrate storage; frequently called a bulb.

Creeping: Growing along or beneath the ground and frequently rooting at the nodes, as in culms and rhizomes.

Crown: Persistent base of a bunchgrass; ring of tissue or hairs at the summit of an organ.

Culm: Aerial stem of a grass; characterized by its structure consisting of a series of solid nodes and hollow or solid internodes.

Cuspidate: Abruptly tipped with a short, sharp, rigid point.

Cylindric: Round in cross section and either longer than wide or wider than long.

Deciduous: Falling away naturally after completing a function.

Decumbent: Growing horizontally along the ground before curving upward.

Decurrent: Extending downward from the point of insertion.

Deltoid: Shaped like an isosceles (equal-sided) triangle with one of the sides at the base.

Dense: Crowded; said of an inflorescence with crowded spikelets or branches.

Dentate: Toothed, usually with large teeth pointed outward.

Denticulate: Toothed with small teeth pointed outward.

Dichotomous: Forked, the branches about equal.

Diffuse: Widely spreading; said of inflorescence branches.

Digitate: Radiating from a common point like fingers from a hand.

Dioecious: Having unisexual flowers, the male and female flowers on different plants.

Disarticulate: To separate at maturity at an existing joint.

Distant: Far from, as opposed to crowded.

Distinct: Separate; not united.

Divaricate: Widely spreading; said of inflorescence branches.

Divergent: Growing away from.

Dorsal: Referring to the back of an organ.

Dorsally compressed: Flattened from back to front with the back rounded and not keeled.

Ellipsoid: Three-dimensional object that is widest at the middle, tapers to ends of the same size, and is round in cross section.

Elliptical: Widest in the middle tapering to ends of the same size.

Emarginate: With a small notch at the tip.

Endemic: Confined to a specific geographic area.

Entire: Edges not toothed, lobed or cut.

Erect: Growing straight upward.

Erose: Edges irregular or jagged.

Exceeding: Longer than.

Excurrent: Continuing beyond.

Exserted: Protruding from some enclosing organ.

Extravaginal: Type of branching in which the shoot breaks out though the side of the sheath.

Falcate: Shaped like a hawk's bill; flat and curved to one side, tapering upward.

Fascicle: Bundle or cluster.

Fertile: Capable of producing seed; either pistillate or perfect; of stamens, capable of producing pollen.

Fibrous: Composed of thread-like structures.

Filiform: Threadlike; long, slender and round in cross section.

Flexuous: Bent alternately in opposite directions, but not strongly so.

Floret: Unit composed of lemma and palea with the enclosed pistil and stamens if any.

Floriferous: Bearing flowers, florets or spikelets.

Flower: Reproductive structure of a grass composed of pistil, stamens or both; sometimes used for the entire floret or spikelet.

Folded: Creased lengthwise along the middle with the upper surface inside; of venation, with the leaf in bud more or less creased lengthwise and the edges approaching each other, but not touching or overlapping.

Fusiform: Spindle shaped; slender but thickest near the middle and tapering toward the ends.

Geniculate: Bent abruptly.

Glabrate: Nearly hairless; becoming hairless with age.

Glabrous: Hairless; sometimes used in place of smooth.

Gland: Structure that produces a fluid.

Glandular pit: Depression that produces a fluid.

Glaucous: Covered with a whitish or bluish waxy substance that rubs off; sometimes loosely applied to any whitish surface.

Globose: Spherical; shaped like a ball.

Glume: One of a pair of bracts found at the base of a spikelet and not containing pistils or stamens; occasionally one or both glumes are absent.

Hairy: Bearing hairs of any kind; of a ligule, composed of hairs for more than half its length.

Hirsute: With moderately coarse, stiff and fairly straight hairs.

Hispid: With stiff, usually sharp hairs.

Hispidulous: With small, stiff, usually sharp hairs.

Hollow: Empty; of a culm, with any air space at all in the central part of an internode.

Hyaline: Thin and transparent or translucent.

Imbricate: Partially overlapping like shingles.

Imperfect: Referring to a flower missing either pistil or stamens.

Included: Not protruding from an enclosing organ.

Indurate: Hard and frequently inflexible.

Inflated: Puffed up.

Inflorescence: Spikelets and the axis or branches bearing them.

Innovation: A short, basal offshoot from the base of a culm or tuft of culms.

Intercostal: Situated between ribs, nerves, or veins.

Internerve: Space between nerves or veins.

Internode: Part of a culm or other structure between two successive nodes.

Interrupted: With the order or continuity broken; of an inflorescence, with gaps in the order of branching; of a collar, with a break in the continuity of its texture, usually at the middle.

Intravaginal: Type of branching in which the shoot emerges from the top of the sheath.

Involucre: Set of bracts, reduced leaves or reduced inflorescence branches arranged below a spikelet or inflorescence.

Involute: Rolled, especially with the edges rolled inward and the upper surface inside.

Joint: Culm node; a rachis or rachilla internode.

Keel: Projecting central rib usually found on the back of an organ and resembling a boat's keel.

Lacerate: With an irregularly torn or jagged edge.

Lanate: Woolly; with long tangled hairs.

Lanceolate: Much longer than wide, widest below the middle and tapering toward both ends (sometimes rounded at the base).

Lateral: On the side.

Laterally compressed: Flattened from the sides.

Lax: Loose; soft and drooping.

Leaf: Organ of a grass plant usually consisting of a sheath surrounding the culm and a blade placed at the top of the sheath and free of the culm.

Lemma: Lower bract of the floret, placed above the glumes with its back toward the outside of the spikelet or away from the rachilla.

Ligule: Membranous or hairy structure on the inside of the leaf at the junction of the sheath and the blade.

Linear: Long and narrow with more or less parallel sides or edges.

Lobed: With rounded projections of the edge of an organ, the adjacent indentations of which extending not more than halfway to the midline or base; with any rounded projection; grouped to exhibit a rounded profile or outline.

Lodicules: Small membranous or fleshy organs situated inside the lemma near its margins which suddenly absorb moisture and swell, forcing the lemma and palea apart and allowing anthesis to occur; thought to be the remnants of petals.

Median line: Line at or near the middle of an organ; especially a line formed by the space between the midvein and its adjacent vein in blades of *Poa*.

Membranous: Thin, soft, flexible and more or less translucent; loosely, of fairly thin texture usually more or less green in color.

Midrib: Main or central vein of an organ.

Monoclinous: Having all flowers perfect.

Monoecious: Having unisexual flowers, the male and female flowers on the same plant.

Mucro: Short, sharp, and abrupt point at the tip of a leaf or other organ.

Mucronate: Tipped with a short, sharp, abrupt point (mucro).

Naked: Lacking an organ or structure that might usually be expected.

Nerve: Prominent vascular vein of an organ, usually arranged parallel to the long axis of the organ and not noticeably branched.

Neuter: Without stamens and pistils.

Nodding: Tipped somewhat away from the vertical; said of inflorescences.

Nodes: Solid point, frequently swollen, on a culm where a leaf or branch is attached; any such point of attachment.

Oblique: At an angle.

Oblong: More or less rectangular; longer than wide with parallel sides or edges.

Obovate: Egg shaped but broadest above the middle.

Obsolete: Reduced in size, sometimes missing entirely, implying better development in the ancestors.

Obtuse: Rounded at the tip.

Open: Loose; not dense; with spreading branches; of a sheath, with the margins separate for at least half their lengths.

Organ: Any individual part of a plant, composed of cells and tissues, and performing some function in the plant.

Oval: Broadly elliptical, the width more than half the length; sometimes used for ovate.

Ovate: Egg-shaped and broadest below the middle.

Ovoid: Three-dimensional egg-shaped object with its largest diameter below the middle.

Palea: Upper bract of the floret, placed above the lemma with its back toward the rachilla.

Panicle: Inflorescence consisting of a main axis with branched branches.

Papery: Thin and stiff yet flexible.

Papillate: Covered with small bumps.

Papillose: Covered with small bumps.

Pectinate: Comb-like.

Pedicel: Stalk of a spikelet.

Pedicellate: Borne of a pedicel.

Peduncle: Stalk of an inflorescence.

Pedunculate: Borne upon a peduncle.

Pendent: Pendulous, hanging, drooping downward.

Pendulous: Hanging or drooping downward.

Perennial: Plant lasting more than two years.

Perfect: Referring to a flower containing both stamens and pistils.

Persistent: Lasting; remaining attached.

Pilose: With long, soft, straight hairs.

Pistil: Seed-producing organ of a plant; the female sex organ of a plant.

Pistillate: Referring to a flower containing only a pistil.

Plano-convex: Flat on one side and rounded on the other.

Plumose: Feather-like; consisting of a main axis with hairs or bristles along the sides.

Produced: Extended.

Proliferous: Bearing vegetative buds or bulblets in the inflorescence.

Prostrate: Flat on the ground.

Pseudoviviparous: A type of reproduction where vegetative offspring (bulbil) begins growing on the maternal plant before dispersal. True pseudovivipary involves vegetative bulbils produced asexually, and is common in some arctic grasses (see also viviparous).

Puberulent: With very short hairs.

Pubescent: With short soft hairs; covered with any kind of hairs.

Pulvinus: Swelling at the base of a sheath or inflorescence, branch which governs how the organ is oriented.

Raceme: Inflorescence consisting of spikelets borne on pedicels from an unbranched rachis.

Racemose: Like a raceme; bearing racemes.

Rachilla: Axis of a spikelet; a stalk-like, sometimes jointed, structure extending above and between the glumes and bearing the florets.

Rachis: Main axis of an inflorescence; loosely, the branches of an inflorescence.

Recurved: Curved backward.

Reduced: Modified through a decrease in size or loss of a part; of a floret, staminate or neuter.

Reflexed: Abruptly bent downward or backward.

Retrorse: Pointed backward or downward.

Rhizomatous: Having underground stems or rhizomes.

Rhizome: Underground stem capable of rooting and producing aerial shoots from the nodes.

Rigid: Stiff; inflexible.

Rolled: With the edges approximate or overlapping and the back rounded; of vernation, the leaf in the bud more or less rounded on the back and the edges touching or overlapping.

Rudiment: Imperfectly developed organ.

Rudimentary: Underdeveloped, implying an early evolutionary stage rather than reduction.

Rugose: Wrinkled.

Scaberulous: Slightly roughened.

Scabridulous: Minutely roughened.

Scabrid: Rough to the touch.

Scabrous: Rough to the touch.

Scarious: Thin, dry, translucent and not green.

Scurfy: Covered with small crusty particles.

Secund: One-sided.

Sericeous: Silky with long, soft, straight, appressed hairs.

Sessile: Without a stalk or pedicel; directly attached by the base.

Setaceous: Bristle-like.

Sheath: Tube-shaped lower part of a leaf placed below the blade and surrounding the culm.

Simple: Unbranched; all in one piece.

Sinuous: Wavy.

Smooth: Not rough to the touch.

Solid: Not hollow.

Spicate: Arranged in or resembling a spike inflorescence.

Spike: Inflorescence consisting of spikelets sessile on an unbranched rachis.

Spikelet: Unit of an inflorescence composed of usually two glumes and one or more florets.

Spikelike: Resembling a spike, especially referring to a dense panicle with very short branches.

Spreading: Horizontal or nearly so.

Stamen: Pollen-producing organ of a flower; the male sex organ of a flower.

Staminate: Bearing stamens only.

Sterile: Producing no seed; producing no pollen; staminate or neuter; producing no flowers.

Stigma: Tip of a pistil, the part that receives the pollen.

Stipe: Very small stalk of an organ; a small prolongation of a rachilla beyond the uppermost floret in the spikelets of some grasses.

Stolon: Modified above-ground prostrate stem capable of rooting and producing shoots from the nodes or the tip; a runner.

Stoloniferous: Producing stolons.

Striate: With fine parallel lines or grooves.

Strigose: With stiff appressed hairs pointing more or less in the same direction.

Strigillose: Minutely strigose.

Style: Stalk-like part of a pistil supporting the stigma.

Sub-: Prefix meaning below, nearly or almost.

Subequal: Nearly equal, usually in length.

Subsessile: Nearly sessile; on a very short stalk or pedicel.

Subtend: To be closely below.

Subulate: Awl-shaped; narrowly triangular and tapering from the base to a sharp point.

Summit: Tip.

Terete: Round in cross section and rather elongate; cylindric.

Terminal: At the upper end.

Throat: Area at the upper margins of a sheath.

Tiller: Shoot growing from the base of a grass plant.

Tomentose: Covered with densely matted woolly hairs.

Trifid: Divided into three parts.

Truncate: Squared off at the tip.

Tubercle: Small rounded bump.

Tuberculate: Bearing small rounded bumps or tubercles.

Tufted: Clustered, especially groups of hairs or caespitose grass plants.

Turgid: Swollen by internal pressure.

Undulate: Gently wavy.

Unisexual: Either staminate or pistillate, but not perfect.

United: Joined together, especially by the edges.

Vegetative: Referring to any part of a plant that is not part of the flower; in reproduction, a means of developing a new plant without seed.

Vein: Vascular tissue of an organ, usually with noticeable branches; sometimes used for nerve.

Vernation: The arrangement of a leaf in the bud.

Vestigial: Much reduced, implying better development in the ancestors.

Villous: With long, soft, frequently wavy but not matted hairs.

Viviparous: A type of reproduction where the offspring (seedling or bulbil) begins growing on the maternal plant before dispersal. True vivipary involves seedlings produced by sexual reproduction, and appears uncommon in arctic grasses (see also pseudoviviparous).

Warm season: Plant which grows and matures later in the growing season.

Webbed: With a cluster of long, soft, tangled hairs; usually referring to hairs at the base of the lemma.

Whorl: Group of structures arranged in a circle around a common axis.

Winter rosette: Cluster of basal leaves forming late in the growing season and producing culms during the following growing season.

References

Alaska Hydrography, 1:1,000,000 [geospatial data]. 1998. Alaska Department of Natural Resources - Information Resource Management Section, Anchorage, Alaska. *http://dnr.alaska.gov/SpatialUtility/SUC.*

Alaska Major Rivers [geospatial data]. 1998. Alaska Department of Natural Resources - Information Resource Management Section, Anchorage, Alaska. *http://dnr.alaska.gov/SpatialUtility/SUC.*

Anderson, J.P. 1974. Anderson's Flora of Alaska and Adjacent Parts of Canada. S.L. Welsh ed. Brigham Young University Press, Provo, Utah. 724 pp.

Barkworth, M.E., K.M. Capels, S. Long, L.K. Anderton, and M.B. Piep, eds. 2007. Magnoliophyta: Commelinidae (in part): Poaceae, part 1, Flora of North America North of Mexico, volume 24. Oxford University Press, New York and Oxford. 911 pp.

Chapin, F.S. III, M.S. Bret-Harte, S.E. Hobbie, and H. Zhong. 1996. Plant functional types as predictors of transient responses of arctic vegetation to global change. Journal of Vegetation Science 7(3):347-358.

Cody, W.J. 2000. Flora of the Yukon Territory, 2nd edition. NRC-CNRC, NRC Research Press, Ottawa, Canada. 669 pp.

GTOPO30 [global digital elevation model (DEM)]. 1996. U.S. Geological Survey EROS Data Center, Sioux Falls, South Dakota. *http://eros.usgs.gov/#/Find_Data/Products_and_Data_Available/gtopo30_info.*

Harrington, H.D. 1977. How to Identify Grasses and Grasslike Plants. The Swallow Press, Inc. Chicago. 142 pp.

Harris, J.G. and M.W. Harris. 1994. Plant Identification Terminology: An Illustrated Glossary. Spring Lake Publishing, Spring Lake, Utah. 197pp.

Hitchcock, A.S. 1951. Manual of the Grasses of the United States. Second Edition. Revised by Agnes Chase. USDA Miscellaneous Publication No. 200. United States Government Printing Office, Washington, D.C. 1,051 pp.

Hultén, E. 1968. Flora of Alaska and Neighboring Territories: A Manual of the Vascular Plants. Stanford University Press, Stanford, California. 1,008 pp.

Lamson-Scribner, F. and E.D. Merrill. 1910. The Grasses of Alaska. Smithsonian Institution, Contributions from the United States National Herbarium, Volume 13, Part 3. Government Printing Office, Washington. pp 47-92 + index. *http://books.google.com/ ebooks?id=Ih4aAAAAYAAJ.*

The Literary Gazette and Journal of Belles Lettres, Arts, Sciences, &c. 1827. Printed by James Moyes, London. p 543. *http://books.google. com/ebooks?id=xR4qhBFpDIIC.*

Perryman, B.L. and Q.D. Skinner. 2007. A Field Guide to Nevada Grasses. Indigenous Rangeland Management Press, Lander, Wyoming. 256 pp.

Polansky, P. and R. Stanton. 1986. Baron Vrangel' visits the Sandwich Islands in 1826 on the Krotkii. The Hawaiian Journal of History 20:13-26. *http://hdl.handle.net/10524/109.*

Skinner, Q.D. 2010. A Field Guide to Wyoming Grasses. Education Resources LLC, Cummings, Georgia. 596 pp.

Soreng, R.J., G. Davidse, P.M. Peterson, F.O. Zuloaga, E.J. Judziewicz, T.S. Filgueiras, and O. Morrone. Viewed 2011. Catalogue of New World Grasses (Poaceae). *http://www.tropicos.org/project/cnwg.*

Vasey, G. 1892. Grasses of the Pacific Slope: Including Alaska and the Adjacent Islands. Plates and Descriptions of the Grasses of California, Oregon, Washington, and the Northwestern Coast, including Alaska, Part I. USDA Division of Botany, Bulletin No. 13. Government Printing Office, Washington. Unnumbered. *http://books.google.com/ ebooks?id=jCcaAAAAYAAJ*

Vasey, G. 1893. Grasses of the Pacific Slope: Including Alaska and the Adjacent Islands. Plates and Descriptions of the grasses of California, Oregon, Washington, and the Northwestern Coast, including Alaska, Part II. USDA Division of Botany, Bulletin No. 13. Government Printing Office, Washington. Unnumbered. *http://books.google.com/ ebooks?id=LNJZMu_7DUwC.*

Wrangell, F. von. 1840. Narrative of an expedition to the Polar Sea, in the years 1820, 1821, 1822, & 1823. Edited by Edward Sabine. James Madden and Co., London. 413 pp. *http://www.archive.org/details/ narrativeofexped00wran.*

Wright, S.J. 1994. Beach Wildrye Planting Guide. State of Alaska, Division of Agriculture, Plant Materials Center, Palmer, Alaska. 27 pp. *http://plants.alaska.gov/publications/pdf/BeachWildryePlantingGuide.pdf.*

Wright, S.J. 2008. A Revegetation Manual for Alaska. Department of Natural Resources, Alaska Plant Materials Center, Palmer, Alaska. 70 pp. + addendum. *http://dnr.alaska.gov/ag/pmcwebgood/TitlePageManualdwt. htm.*

Wright, S.J. and P.K. Czapla. 2010. Alaska Coastal Revegetation and Erosion Control Guide. Alaska Department of Natural Resources, Division of Agriculture, Plant Materials Center, Palmer, Alaska. 177 pp. + appendices. *http://plants.alaska.gov/reveg/index.php*

Species Index

375

376

Notes

Notes